The Wedding Book

with the Marriage Service ASB 1980

Edited by Michael Perry and Norman Warren

Jubilate : Marshall Pickering : CPAS

Marshall Morgan & Scott,
Middlesex House, 34–42 Cleveland Street, London W1P 5FB

First published in 1989 by Marshall Morgan & Scott Publications Ltd., part of the Marshall Pickering Holdings Group, a subsidiary of the Zondervan Corporation.

British Library Cataloguing in Publication Data
The Wedding Book
  1. Hymns, English
  I. Perry, Michael II. Warren, Norman

  ISBN 0-551-01806-2

Also from Marshall Pickering:
The Wedding Book: words edition – pack of 25 copies. ISBN 0-551-01808-9

Music and text set by Barnes Music Engraving Ltd., East Sussex.
Printed in Great Britain by The Bath Press, Avon.

CONTENTS

Preface

THE MARRIAGE SERVICE
From *The Alternative Service Book 1980*

AT THE INTRODUCTION
* indicates descant available

God's grace and providence
Amazing grace – how sweet the sound (Amazing grace) – 19
For the beauty of the earth (England's Lane, Ashburton) – 20
Morning has broken like the first morning (Bunessan) – 21
All things bright and beautiful (All things bright, Royal Oak) – 22
Great is your faithfulness (Great is thy faithfulness) – 23
Jesus is Lord – 24

Jesus at a wedding
Jesus come! for we invite you
   (Unser Herrscher*, Westminster Abbey*, Oriel*, Kinessburn) – 25
Jesus, Lord, we pray (Arnstadt) – 26
To Cana's wedding feast (Laudes Domini) – 27

AT THE MARRIAGE

Psalm 23
The king of love my shepherd is (The Followers*, Dominus regit me) – 28
The Lord's my shepherd (Brother James' Air, Crimond*) – 29

Psalm 34
Through all the changing scenes of life (Wiltshire*) – 30

Psalm 46
God is our strength and refuge (Dam Busters march) – 31

Psalm 67
God of mercy, God of grace (Heathlands) – 32
May God be gracious (Ellers, Universa laus) – 33
Mercy, blessing, favour, grace (Binscombe, Impact, Urchfont) – 34

Psalm 84
How lovely is your dwelling-place (Hampton Hill, Melchbourne) – 35

Psalm 98
Sing to God new songs of worship (Ode to Joy) – 36

Psalm 104
O worship the king (Hanover*) – 37

Psalm 121
I will lift up my eyes to the hills — 38
I lift my eyes to the quiet hills (Davos*) — 39
Unto the hills around me (Sandon) — 40

Psalm 128
Bless all who trust in God (Franconia, Doncaster) — 41
Blessed are those who fear the Lord (Culbach, Innocents) — 42
To set their hearts on God (Sandys) — 43

Psalm 133
How good a thing it is (Venice, Franconia) — 44

BEFORE, OR DURING THE PRAYERS

The congregation pray
Jesus the Lord of love and life (Warrington, Tallis' Canon) — 45
Lord Jesus Christ, invited guest and saviour (O perfect love) — 46
O perfect love — 47
God be with them (Buckland) — 48
May Christ, the Lord of Cana's Feast (Repton) — 49
Praise God, the hour has come (Monks Gate) — 50
To God's loving-kindness (Oakley) — 51

The couple pray
Father, we adore you — 52
Happy are they — wedding version (Binchester) — 53
Help us to help each other (St Hugh) — 54
May the mind of Christ — wedding version (St Leonard's) — 55
Eternal Father, Lord of life (Bishopsgarth) — 56
Father, hear the prayer we offer (Gott will's machen) — 57
God of all living (Bunessan) — 58
Happy the home (Strength and stay) — 59
Join with us, friends, today (Down Ampney*) — 60
Take our lives and let them be (Consecration) — 61

For God the Father's guidance/protection/presence
Guide me, O my great redeemer (Cwm Rhondda) — 62
Lead us, heavenly Father — revised version (Mannheim) — 63
Lead us, heavenly Father — standard version (Mannheim) — 64
Lord Jesus, you have won our hearts (Morden) — 65
Lord of all hopefulness (Slane) — 66

Lord of creation (Bunessan) – 67
How blessed are those who trust in God (Church Triumphant) – 68

For the mind of Christ
May the mind of Christ – standard version (St Leonard's) – 69
Make me a channel of your peace (St Francis) – 70

For the Spirit's blessing
Breathe on me, breath of God (Carlisle*, Saints Alive, Trentham) – 71
Dear Lord and Father of mankind (Repton) – 72
Come down, O Love divine (Down Ampney*) – 73
O Holy Spirit, breathe on me (O Holy Spirit) – 74
O Lord, who came from realms above (Hereford) – 75
O thou who camest from above (Hereford) – 76
Spirit of God unseen as the wind (Skye Boat Song) – 77

Dedication
Christ is our corner-stone (Darwall's 148th*) – 78
Lord of all power – wedding version (Slane) – 79
Day by day – 80
Fill now my life (Richmond*) – 81
Lord Jesus Christ, you have come to us (Living Lord) – 82
All for Jesus (All for Jesus) – 83
Take my life and let it be – revised version (Nottingham, Lubeck, Emma*) – 84
We trust in you (Finlandia) – 85
When all your mercies, O my God (Contemplation) – 86

Prayer/The Lord's Prayer/Fellowship
May the grace of God our saviour (Halton Holgate, Waltham) – 87
Father God in heaven (Kum ba yah) – 88
Bind us together, Lord (Bind us together) – 89
Let there be love shared among us (Let there be love) – 90
Like a mighty river flowing (Quem pastores laudavere, Old Yeavering*) – 91
What a friend we have in Jesus (Blaenwern, Converse) – 92

FOR THE END OF THE SERVICE – CELEBRATION

Thanksgiving, praise and worship
Now thank we all our God (Nun danket*, Gracias) – 93
Praise the Lord, you heavens (Austria*) – 94
Praise to the Lord the almighty (Lobe den Herren*) – 95
Sing praise to the Lord (Laudate Dominum*) – 96

APPENDICES (MUSIC EDITION ONLY)

NOTES AND SUGGESTIONS

To the Musician
Suggested anthems – (Music Edition only)
Suggested performance songs – (Music Edition only)
Suggested organ voluntaries – (Music Edition only)

To the Bride and Groom
Using the service
Choosing the hymns
Choosing the music

Legal Information

INDEXES

PREFACE

The churches offer a service to the community by 'solemnising' marriage. Some couples who are not practising Christians nevertheless ask for Christian marriage. This apparent challenge to the church's integrity is met in various ways: by insisting upon a course of instruction where the real issues of Christian dedication and commitment to life-time faithfulness can be met and examined; by treating the encounter with the couple as an opportunity for evangelism; or by treating all as equally Christian (be they Muslim, Hindu or atheist), so that the Christian way is never really considered, and the couple pass through their wedding experience satisfied by the comfort of tradition but untouched by the expectations of the Gospel.

How great is the delight of those who truly understand their marriage as something done in the sight of God, their wedding service as a public dedication both to each other and to Christ's service! Only a few couples see it quite that way. Yet many others, who may be just beginning to perceive the spiritual relationships of life, nevertheless want to achieve faithfulness, domestic harmony, a mutual love and service in their marriage, a steady environment for rearing and training children, and a constructive service to the community. Such idealism is surely to be encouraged. To this, the spiritual dimension can be added. The wedding service must reflect all these laudable desires – what the couple want to say to God. And it must be the opportunity for the couple to receive God's grace – what God wants to say to them.

The new Marriage Service (ASB 1980) of the Church of England, printed in *The Wedding Book*, has been received almost invariably with approval. It combines the merit of simplicity – clarity of expression – with a happy theology of marriage. It expresses precisely those ideals of which we have spoken – and more. The minister using it can be secure in the knowledge that here is the best source available. But it is what is added to that service which can make or mar – for instance, the choice of hymns.

The poem 'And did those feet . .', Blake's caustic comment on the scars of the industrial revolution, is enhanced by an exciting tune (Parry's 'Jerusalem') but has little to say about marriage – or God. The patriotic song, 'I vow to thee my country' may be apt for princes and old soldiers, but is a spiritual waste of space at a wedding. The solo, 'Ave Maria' may cover the whispers at the signing of the register and so render a practical service, but it is seldom a spiritual service – if only because Latin is rarely understood. All these things are asked for at Weddings. And ministers or organists, who, quite properly do not wish to be a kill-joy on a festive occasion, too often capitulate. Where this happens the minister of God becomes merely a master of ceremonies.

The Wedding Book meets the dilemma by providing tried and apposite Christian words to melodies which are in demand. A good many new wedding hymns set to best-known hymn tunes are also published here together for the first time. All the other most popular wedding choices have been included after wide research into what churches were actually using at weddings. *The Wedding Book* omits verses that regularly cause trouble, either because they are 'giggle-making' ('Breathe through the heats of our desire'), or because they are now hugely inappropriate ('The meadows where we play; the rushes by the water we gather every day'). Four or five of the hymns are offered in alternative versions, with the first occurence specially adapted for wedding use (as in 'Lord Jesus Christ, we have come to you'). There is also a selection of metrical versions of the appointed psalms.

Ministers and organists will find the contents page very helpful in assisting a couple to choose hymns. The first section offers hymns of approach, as well as those that match the opening themes of the ASB Marriage Service; the second section relates to the psalms; the third section to the prayers; and the last section groups together hymns of celebration.

The Wedding Book is designed as much to suit weddings with a choir present, as those where there is no-one except the accompanist to lead the singing. So there are special arrangements for choirs — if present. Also, in *The Wedding Book: Music Edition*, we have included some simple pieces as a resource for the musician. Accomplished players will have other access to music, but even so many will be grateful for these impromptu pieces for use when the bride is late, or the vicar takes too long in the vestry! Their basic arrangements may be elaborated, the marked notes applied to the pedals etc. The cheerful reluctant organist will find they are manna from heaven!

The uncomplicated words edition of *The Wedding Book* is available in two basic formats: one hard-wearing, for regular use at weddings in church; the second, much more like a traditional wedding programme, for the bride and groom to purchase in sufficient quantities for their guests. These can be inserted into over-printed covers.

We are grateful to all those who contributed to *The Wedding Book* — not least to those members of the Liturgical Commission of the Church of England who designed and developed the service, but also to the Jubilate group of authors and musicians who gave their skill and expertise to the project. We commend their work and this volume to brides, grooms, ministers and musicians and offer it humbly to the service of God in the churches.

Michael Perry, Rector of Eversley
Norman Warren, Archdeacon of Rochester
Editors

The Marriage Service

THE INTRODUCTION

1 **Stand**
The bride and bridegroom stand before the priest.
THIS SENTENCE (see also numbers 109i and 109ii) may be used.

> God is love, and those who live in love, live in
> God: and God lives in them. *1 John 4.16*

2 *The priest may say*

> The Lord be with you
> **All   and also with you.**

3 Priest   God our Father,
> you have taught us through your Son
> that love is the fulfilling of the law.
> Grant to your servants
> that, loving one another,
> they may continue in your love
> until their lives' end;
> through Jesus Christ our Lord. **Amen.**

4 **Sit**
One or more READINGS may be used (see section 22 and page xxv).
If there are two or three readings, A PSALM (see section 23 and
numbers 28–44) or A HYMN may be sung between them.

5 *A SERMON may be preached.*

THE MARRIAGE

6   *The bride and bridegroom stand before the priest, and the priest says*

We have come together in the presence of God, to witness the marriage of N and N, to ask his blessing on them, and to share in their joy. Our Lord Jesus Christ was himself a guest at a wedding in Cana of Galilee, and through his Spirit he is with us now.

The Scriptures teach us that marriage is a gift of God in creation and a means of his grace, a holy mystery in which man and woman become one flesh. It is God's purpose that, as husband and wife give themselves to each other in love throughout their lives, they shall be united in that love as Christ is united with his Church.

Marriage is given, that husband and wife may comfort and help each other, living faithfully together in need and in plenty, in sorrow and in joy. It is given, that with delight and tenderness they may know each other in love, and, through the joy of their bodily union, may strengthen the union of their hearts and lives. It is given, that they may have children and be blessed in caring for them and bringing them up in accordance with God's will, to his praise and glory.

In marriage husband and wife belong to one another, and they begin a new life together in the community. It is a way of life that all should honour; and it must not be undertaken carelessly, lightly, or selfishly, but reverently, responsibly, and after serious thought.

This is the way of life, created and hallowed by God, that N and N are now to begin. They will each give their consent to the other; they will join hands and exchange solemn vows, and in token of this they will give and receive a ring.

Therefore, on this their wedding day we pray with them, that, strengthened and guided by God, they may fulfil his purpose for the whole of their earthly life together.

7 *The priest says to the congregation*

> But first I am required to ask anyone present who knows a reason why these persons may not lawfully marry, to declare it now.

8 *The priest says to the couple*

> The vows you are about to take are to be made in the name of God, who is judge of all and who knows all the secrets of our hearts: therefore if either of you knows a reason why you may not lawfully marry, you must declare it now.

9 **Stand**
The priest says to the bridegroom

> N, will you take N to be your wife? Will you love her, comfort her, honour and protect her, and, forsaking all others, be faithful to her as long as you both shall live?

He answers

> I will.

10 *The priest says to the bride*

> N, will you take N to be your husband? Will you love him, comfort him, honour and protect him, and, forsaking all others, be faithful to him as long as you both shall live?

She answers

> I will.

11   *Either A*

The priest may receive the bride from the hands of her father.
The bride and bridegroom face each other.
The bridegroom takes the bride's right hand in his, and says

> I, *N*, take you, *N*,
> to be my wife,
> to have and to hold
> from this day forward;
> for better, for worse,
> for richer, for poorer,
> in sickness and in health,
> to love and to cherish,
> till death us do part,
> according to God's holy law;
> and this is my solemn vow.

They loose hands
The bride takes the bridegroom's right hand in hers, and says

> I, *N*, take you, *N*,
> to be my husband,
> to have and to hold
> from this day forward;
> for better, for worse,
> for richer, for poorer,
> in sickness and in health,
> to love and to cherish,
> till death us do part,
> according to God's holy law;
> and this is my solemn vow.

They loose hands.

The service continues at section 13 on page xvi / Marriage 292

---

12 *or B*

The priest may receive the bride from the hands of her father.
The bride and bridegroom face each other.
The bridegroom takes the bride's right hand in his, and says

> I, *N,* take you, *N,*
> to be my wife,
> to have and to hold
> from this day forward;
> for better, for worse,
> for richer, for poorer,
> in sickness and in health,
> to love, cherish, and worship,
> till death us do part,
> according to God's holy law;
> and this is my solemn vow.

They loose hands.
The bride takes the bridegroom's right hand in hers, and says

> I, *N,* take you, *N,*
> to be my husband,
> to have and to hold
> from this day forward;
> for better, for worse,
> for richer, for poorer,
> in sickness and in health,
> to love, cherish, and obey,
> till death us do part,
> according to God's holy law;
> and this is my solemn vow.

They loose hands.

---

13   *The priest receives the ring(s). He says*

> Heavenly Father, by your blessing, let *this ring* be to N
> and N a symbol of unending love and faithfulness, to
> remind them of the vow and covenant which they have
> made this day; through Jesus Christ our Lord. **Amen.**

14   *The bridegroom places the ring on the fourth finger of the bride's left
     hand, and holding it there, says*

> I give you this ring
> as a sign of our marriage.
> With my body I honour you,
> all that I am I give to you,
> and all that I have I share with you,
> within the love of God,
> Father, Son, and Holy Spirit.

15   *If only one ring is used, before they loose hands the bride says*

> I receive this ring
> as a sign of our marriage.
> With my body I honour you,
> all that I am I give to you,
> and all that I have I share with you,
> within the love of God,
> Father, Son, and Holy Spirit.

16   *If rings are exchanged, they loose hands and the bride places a ring on
     the fourth finger of the bridegroom's left hand, and holding it there, says*

> I give you this ring
> as a sign of our marriage.
> With my body I honour you,
> all that I am I give to you,
> and all that I have I share with you,
> within the love of God,
> Father, Son, and Holy Spirit.

17　*The priest addresses the people.*

> In the presence of God, and before this congregation, *N*
> and *N* have given their consent and made their
> marriage vows to each other. They have declared their
> marriage by the joining of hands and by the giving and
> receiving of *a ring*. I therefore proclaim that they are
> husband and wife.

18　*The priest joins their right hands together and says*

> That which God has joined together,
> let not man divide.

19　*The congregation remain standing.*
　　The husband and wife kneel, and the priest blesses them.

> God the Father,
> God the Son,
> God the Holy Spirit,
> bless, preserve, and keep you;
> the Lord mercifully grant you the
> 　　riches of his grace,
> that you may please him both in body and soul,
> and, living together in faith and love,
> may receive the blessings of eternal life. **Amen.**

20　*These acclamations may be used (see also numbers 110i and 110ii).*

Priest　Blessed are you, heavenly Father:
All　　**You give joy to bridegroom and bride.**

Priest　Blessed are you, Lord Jesus Christ:
All　　**You have brought new life to mankind.**

Priest　Blessed are you, Holy Spirit of God:
All　　**You bring us together in love.**

Priest　Blessed be the Father, Son, and Holy Spirit:
All　　**One God, to be praised for ever. Amen.**

21 **Sit**
THE REGISTRATION of the marriage takes place now or at the end
of the service.

22 If sections 4 and 5 have been omitted, at least ONE READING is used
here (see page xxv), and a SERMON may be preached.

23 **Stand**
One or more of the following PSALMS (see also index to psalm
versions) are used, or A HYMN may be sung.

PSALM 67 (see also numbers 32–34)

1 Let God be gracious to ˈ us and ˈ bless us:
   and make his ˈ face ˈ shine upˈon us,

2 that your ways may be ˈ known on ˈ earth:
   your liberating ˈ power · aˈmong all ˈ nations.

3 Let the peoples ˈ praise you · O ˈ God:
   let ˈ all the ˈ peoples ˈ praise you.

4 Let the nations be ˈ glad and ˈ sing:
   for you judge the peoples with integrity
   and govern the ˈ nations · upˈon ˈ earth.

5 Let the peoples ˈ praise you · O ˈ God:
   let ˈ all the ˈ peoples ˈ praise you.

6 Then the earth will ˈ yield its ˈ fruitfulness:
   and ˈ God our ˈ God will ˈ bless us.

†7 God ˈ shall ˈ bless us:
   and all the ˈ ends · of the ˈ earth will ˈ fear him.

   Glory to the Father and ˈ to the ˈ Son:
   and ˈ to the ˈ Holy ˈ Spirit;
 as it was in the beˈginning is ˈ now:
   and shall be for ˈ ever. ˈ Aˈmen.

PSALM 121 (see also numbers 38–40)

1 I lift up my ˌ eyes · to the ˌ hills:
   but ˌ where · shall I ˌ find ˌ help?

2 My help ˌ comes · from the ˌ Lord:
   who has ˌ made ˌ heaven · and ˌ earth.

3 He will not suffer your ˌ foot to ˌ stumble:
   and he who watches ˌ over · you ˌ will not ˌ sleep.

4 Be sure he who has ˌ charge of ˌ Israel:
   will ˌ neither ˌ slumber · nor ˌ sleep.

5 The Lord himˌself · is your ˌ keeper:
   the Lord is your defence upˌon your ˌ right ˌ hand;

6 the sun shall not ˌ strike you · by ˌ day:
   nor ˌ shall the ˌ moon by ˌ night.

7 The Lord will defend you from ˌ all ˌ evil:
   it is ˌ he · who will ˌ guard your ˌ life.

8 The Lord will defend your going out and your ˌ
   coming ˌ in:
   from this time ˌ forward · for ˌ everˌmore.

   Glory to the Father and ˌ to the ˌ Son:
   and ˌ to the ˌ Holy ˌ Spirit;
   as it was in the beˌginning is ˌ now:
   and shall be for ˌ ever. ˌ Aˌmen.

PSALM 128 (see also numbers 41–43)

1 Blessèd is everyone who ˌ fears the ˌ Lord:
   and walks in the ˌ confine ˌ of his ˌ ways.

2 You will eat the ˌ fruit of · your ˌ labours:
   happy shall you ˌ be and ˌ all · shall go ˌ well with you.

3 Your wife withˌin your ˌ house:
   shall ˌ be · as a ˌ fruitful ˌ vine;

4 your children aˌround your ˌ table:
   like the fresh ˌ shoots ˌ of the ˌ olive.

5 Behold thus shall the ˈ man be ˈ blessed:
    who ˈ lives · in the ˈ fear ˈ of the ˈ Lord.

6 May the Lord so ˈ bless you · from ˈ Zion:
    that you see Jerusalem in prosperity ˈ‿
    all the ˈ days of · your ˈ life.

†7 May you see your ˈ children's ˈ children:
    and in ˈ Israel ˈ let there · be ˈ peace.

   Glory to the Father and ˈ to the ˈ Son:
       and ˈ to the ˈ Holy ˈ Spirit;
   as it was in the beˈginning is ˈ now:
       and shall be for ˈ ever. ˈ Aˈmen.

THE PRAYERS

24 **Kneel**
   The husband and wife kneel before the holy table.

   Priest   Almighty God,
                you send your Holy Spirit
                to be the life and light of all your people.
                Open the hearts of these your children
                    to the riches of his grace,
                that they may bring forth the fruit of the Spirit
                in love and joy and peace;
                through Jesus Christ our Lord. **Amen.**

25 *Either or both of these prayers are said.*

26 Priest   Heavenly Father,
                maker of all things,
                you enable us to share in the work of creation.
                Bless this couple in the gift and care of children,
                that their home may be a place of love,
                    security, and truth,
                and their children grow up
                    to know and love you in your Son
                Jesus Christ our Lord. **Amen.**

27 Priest   Lord and Saviour Jesus Christ,
              who shared at Nazareth the life of an
                  earthly home:
              reign in the home of these your servants
                  as Lord and King;
              give them grace to minister to others
                  as you have ministered to men,
              and grant that by deed and word
              they may be witnesses of your
                  saving love
              to those among whom they live;
              for the sake of your holy name. **Amen.**

28 *Other prayers may be said here (see sections 31–38)*

29 Priest   As our Saviour taught us, so we pray.
    All   **Our Father in heaven,**
              hallowed be your name,
              your kingdom come,
              your will be done,
              on earth as in heaven.
              Give us today our daily bread.
              Forgive us our sins
              as we forgive those who sin against us.
              Lead us not into temptation
              but deliver us from evil.

              For the kingdom, the power, and the glory
                  are yours
              now and for ever. Amen.

30 *The priest blesses the couple and the congregation, saying*

              God the Holy Trinity make you strong in faith
              and love, defend you on every side, and guide
              you in truth and peace; and the blessing of God
              almighty, the Father, the Son, and the Holy
              Spirit, be among you and remain with you
              always. **Amen.**

ADDITIONAL PRAYERS

31   Almighty God, giver of life and love, bless N and N,
whom you have now joined in Christian marriage.
Grant them wisdom and devotion in their life together,
that each may be to the other a strength in need, a
comfort in sorrow, and a companion in joy. So unite
their wills in your will, and their spirits in your Spirit,
that they live and grow together in love and peace all
the days of their life; through Jesus Christ our Lord.
Amen.

32   Almighty and most merciful Father,
the strength of all who put their trust in you:
we pray that, as you have brought N
  and N together by your providence,
so you will enrich them by your grace;
that those vows which they have made
  to one another in your sight,
they may truly and faithfully perform;
through Jesus Christ our Lord. **Amen.**

33   Almighty Father,
you have created all mankind
to glorify you in body and in spirit.
Give these your children joy in
  one another,
as living temples of the Holy Spirit,
and bring them by this joy to know
  and share
in your creative and redeeming love;
through Jesus Christ our Lord, **Amen.**

34   Eternal God, true and loving Father, in holy marriage
you make your servants one. May their life together
witness to your love in this troubled world; may unity
overcome division, forgiveness heal injury, and joy
triumph over sorrow, through Jesus Christ our Lord.
Amen.

35   We praise you, Father, that you have made all things, and hold all things in being. In the beginning you created the universe, and made mankind in your own likeness: because it was not good for them to be alone, you created them male and female; and in marriage you join man and woman as one flesh, teaching us that what you have united may never be divided.

We praise you that you have made this holy mystery a symbol of the marriage of Christ with his Church, and an image of your eternal covenant with your people.

And we pray for your blessing on this man and this woman, who come before you as partners and heirs together of your promises. Grant that this man may love his wife as Christ loves his bride the Church, giving himself for it and cherishing it as his own flesh; and grant that this woman may love her husband and follow the example of those holy women whose praises are sung in the Scriptures. Strengthen them with your grace that they may be witnesses of Christ to others; let them live to see their children's children, and bring them at the last to fullness of life with your saints in the kingdom of heaven; through Jesus Christ our Lord. **Amen.**

36   Heavenly Father,
we thank you that in our earthly lives
you speak to us of your eternal life:
we pray that through their marriage
N and N
may know you more clearly,
love you more dearly,
and follow you more nearly,
day by day,
through Jesus Christ our Lord. **Amen.**

37   O God of love, look mercifully upon *N* and *N* in the
new life which they begin together this day. Unite
them evermore in your love. Keep them faithful to the
vows they have made one to the other. Strengthen
them with every good gift. And let your peace be with
them, now and always; for the sake of Jesus Christ our
Lord. **Amen.**

38   Almighty God, our heavenly Father,
who gave marriage to be a source of
    blessing to mankind,
we thank you for the joys of family life.
May we know your presence and peace
    in our homes;
fill them with your love,
and use them for your glory;
through Jesus Christ our Lord. **Amen.**

AT A MARRIAGE : READINGS

OLD TESTAMENT READING

Genesis 1.26-28, 31a NEB

God said, 'Let us make man in our image and likeness to rule
the fish in the sea, the birds of heaven, the cattle, all wild
animals on earth, and all reptiles that crawl upon the earth.'
So God created man in his own image; in the image of God he
created him; male and female he created them. God blessed them
and said to them, 'Be fruitful and increase, fill the earth and
subdue it, rule over the fish in the sea, the birds of heaven,
and every living thing that moves upon the earth.' So it was;
and God saw all that he had made, and it was very good.

NEW TESTAMENT READING (EPISTLE)

New Testament *Romans 12.1, 2, 9-13 NEB*

My brothers, I implore you by God's mercy to offer your very
selves to him: a living sacrifice, dedicated and fit for his
acceptance, the worship offered by mind and heart. Adapt yourselves
no longer to the pattern of this present world, but let your minds
be remade and your whole nature thus transformed. Then you will be
able to discern the will of God, and to know what is good, acceptable
and perfect.

Love in all sincerity, loathing evil and clinging to the good.
Let love for our brotherhood breed warmth of mutual affection.
Give pride of place to one another in esteem.

With unflagging energy, in ardour of spirit, serve the Lord.

Let hope keep you joyful; in trouble stand firm;
persist in prayer.

Contribute to the needs of God's people,
and practise hospitality.

or *1 Corinthians 13 NEB*

I may speak in tongues of men or of angels, but if I am without love,
I am a sounding gong or a clanging cymbal. I may have the gift of
prophecy, and know every hidden truth; I may have faith strong enough
to move mountains; but if I have no love, I am nothing. I may dole out
all I possess, or even give my body to be burnt, but if I have no love,
I am none the better.

Love is patient; love is kind and envies no one. Love is never boastful,
nor conceited, nor rude; never selfish, not quick to take offence. Love
keeps no score of wrongs; does not gloat over other men's sins, but
delights in the truth. There is nothing love cannot face; there is no
limit to its faith, its hope, and its endurance.

Love will never come to an end. Are there prophets? their work will be
over. Are there tongues of ecstasy? they will cease. Is there knowledge?
it will vanish away; for our knowledge and our prophecy alike are partial,
and the partial vanishes when wholeness comes. When I was a child, my
speech, my outlook and my thoughts were all childish. When I grew up, I
had finished with childish things. Now we see only puzzling reflections
in a mirror, but then we shall see face to face. My knowledge is now
partial, then it will be whole, like God's knowledge of me. In a word,
there are three things that last for ever: faith, hope and love;
but the greatest of them all is love.

or *Ephesians 3.14-end RSV*

I bow my knees before the Father, from whom every family in heaven and on
earth is named, that according to the riches of his glory he may grant
you to be strengthened with might through his Spirit in the inner man,
and that Christ may dwell in your hearts through faith; that you, being
rooted and grounded in love, may have power to comprehend with all the
saints what is the breadth and length and height and depth, and to know
the love of Christ which surpasses knowledge, that you may be filled with
the fullness of God.

Now to him who by the power at work within us is able to do far more
abundantly than all that we ask or think, to him be glory in the church
and in Christ Jesus to all generations, for ever and ever. Amen.

or *Ephesians 5.21-33 JB*

Give way to one another in obedience to Christ. Wives should regard their
husbands as they regard the Lord, since as Christ is head of the Church
and saves the whole body, so is a husband the head of his wife; and as the
Church submits to Christ, so should wives to their husbands, in everything.
Husbands should love their wives just as Christ loved the Church and
sacrificed himself for her to make her holy. He made her clean by washing
her in water with a form of words, so that when he took her to himself
she would be glorious, with no speck or wrinkle or anything like that, but
holy and faultless. In the same way, husbands must love their wives as they
love their own bodies; for a man to love his wife is for him to love
himself. A man never hates his own body, but he feeds it and looks after
it; and that is the way Christ treats the Church, because it is his body —
and we are its living parts. For this reason, a man must leave his father
and mother and be joined to his wife, and the two will become one body.
This mystery has many implications; but I am saying it applies to Christ
and the Church. To sum up; you too, each one of you, must love his wife
as he loves himself; and let every wife respect her husband.

or *Colossians 3.12-17 RSV*

Put on then, as God's chosen ones, holy and beloved, compassion, kindness,
lowliness, meekness, and patience, forbearing one another and, if one has
a complaint against another, forgiving each other; as the Lord has forgiven
you, so you also must forgive. And above all these put on love, which binds
everything together in perfect harmony. And let the peace of Christ rule
in your hearts, to which indeed you were called in the one body. And be
thankful. Let the word of Christ dwell in you richly, as you teach and
admonish one another in all wisdom, and as you sing psalms and hymns and
spiritual songs with thankfulness in your hearts to God. And whatever you
do, in word or deed, do everything in the name of the Lord Jesus, giving
thanks to God the Father through him.

or *1 John 4.7-12 JB*

My dear people,
let us love one another
since love comes from God
and everyone who loves is begotten by God
        and knows God.
Anyone who fails to love can never have known God,
because God is love.
God's love for us was revealed
when God sent into the world his only Son
so that we could have life through him;
this is the love I mean:
not our love for God,
but God's love for us when he sent his Son
to be the sacrifice that takes our sins away.
My dear people,
since God has loved us so much,
we too should love one another.
No one has ever seen God;
but as long as we love one another
God will live in us
and his love will be complete in us.

GOSPEL

Gospel *Matthew 7.21, 24-27 RSV*

Jesus said, 'Not every one who says to me, "Lord, Lord," shall enter the kingdom of heaven, but he who does the will of my Father who is in heaven.'

'Every one then who hears these words of mine and does them will be like a wise man who built his house upon the rock; and the rain fell, and the floods came, and the winds blew and beat upon that house, but it did not fall, because it had been founded on the rock. And every one who hears these words of mine and does not do them will be like a foolish man who built his house upon the sand; and the rain fell, and the floods came, and the winds blew and beat against that house, and it fell; and great was the fall of it.'

or *Mark 10.6-9 NEB*

Jesus said, 'In the beginning, at the creation, God made them male and female. For this reason a man shall leave his father and mother, and be made one with his wife; and the two shall become one flesh. It follows that they are no longer two individuals: they are one flesh. What God has joined together, man must not separate.'

or *John 2.1-11 NEB*

On the third day there was a wedding at Cana-in-Galilee. The mother of Jesus was there, and Jesus and his disciples were guests also. The wine gave out, so Jesus' mother said to him, 'They have no wine left.' He answered, 'Your concern, mother, is not mine. My hour has not yet come.' His mother said to the servants, 'Do whatever he tells you.' There were six stone water-jars standing near, of the kind used for Jewish rites of purification; each held from twenty to thirty gallons. Jesus said to the servants, 'Fill the jars with water,' and they filled them to the brim. 'Now draw some off,' he ordered, 'and take it to the steward of the feast'; and they did so. The steward tasted the water now turned into wine, not knowing its source; though the servants who had drawn the water knew. He hailed the bridegroom and said, 'Everyone serves the best wine first, and waits until the guests have drunk freely before serving the poorer sort; but you have kept the best wine till now.'

This deed at Cana-in-Galilee is the first of the signs by which Jesus revealed his glory and led his disciples to believe in him.

or *John 15.9-12 JB*

Jesus said,
'As the Father has loved me,
so I have loved you.
Remain in my love.
If you keep my commandments
you will remain in my love,
just as I have kept my Father's commandments
and remain in his love.
I have told you this
so that my own joy may be in you
and your joy be complete.
This is my commandment:
love one another,
as I have loved you.'

Notes from the Alternative Service Book 1980

GENERAL NOTES

Distinctions in the Text Sections of services with numbers in italic may be omitted. Where a number of options are included in a mandatory part of a service, the rubric governing the options is numbered in black, but the texts themselves are numbered in italic. Texts in bold type are to be said by the congregation.

Saying and singing Where rubrics indicate that a section is to be 'said', this must be understood to include 'or sung' and vice versa.

Posture Wherever a certain posture is particularly appropriate, it is indicated in the left-hand margin. At all other points local custom may be established and followed.

Biblical Passages The sentences, psalms, and readings may be read in any duly authorized version.

Prayer Book Texts Where parts of a service are sung to well-known settings, the traditional words for which they were composed may be used.

The Lord's Prayer On any occasion the Lord's Prayer may be used in its modern form (as printed in this service), or in its modified form (as in Holy Communion Rite B ASB), or in its traditional form (as in the Book of Common Prayer).

Collect Endings In the case of any collect ending with the words 'Christ our Lord', the Minister may at his discretion add the longer ending:
> 'who is alive and reigns with you and the Holy Spirit, one God, now and for ever'.

Hymns Various points are indicated for the singing of hymns; but, if occasion requires, they may be sung at other points also.

Chanting Psalms and Canticles

(a) Breath is to be taken at asterisks, and at the end of lines except where the pointing clearly forbids it, or when the sign ‿ is used to indicate a 'carry-over'.

A shorter break, or 'mental comma', made without taking breath, is indicated by an extra space between words.

(b) The centred dot indicates how the syllables within a bar are to be divided, when there are more than two.

(c) The sign † indicates use of the second half of a double chant.

(d) A double space between verses indicates that a change of chant is appropriate.

(e) The final 'ed' should not be pronounced as a separate syllable unless marked with an accent (e.g. blessèd).

(f) Verses enclosed within square brackets may be omitted.

(g) The Jewish doxologies which conclude Books 1 to 4 of the Psalter (see Psalms 41, 72, 89, 106) are enclosed within brackets. When a Christian doxology is used, they may be omitted.

MARRIAGE SERVICE NOTES

The Banns The banns are to be published in the church on three Sundays at the time of Divine Service by the officiant in the form set out in the Book of Common Prayer or in the following form: I publish the banns of marriage between N of . . . and N of . . . This is the first (second) (third) time of asking. If any of you know any reason in law why these persons may not marry each other you are to declare it now.

Hymns and Canticles These may be used at suitable points during the service. Sections 1 (see also numbers 109i and 109ii), 20 (see also numbers 110i and 110ii), and 23 (see also numbers 32–34) may be sung if so desired.

Seating It is recommended that chairs should be provided for the bride and bridegroom during the readings and sermon.

The Readings At least one reading must be used, either at the beginning of the service (section 4) or after the Marriage (section 22); but readings must not be used at both places. At Holy Communion there are two readings, of which the Gospel must be one. Suggested readings are printed on pages xxv–xxvii / ASB pages 302 f. and 923 f.

The Giving Away This ceremony is optional. If the bride is not given away by her father, this may be done by another member of her family, or by a friend representing the family.

The Vows In sections 11 and 12 the vows A and the vows B are not interchangeable. Either the vows A or the vows B must be used throughout. Before the day of the marriage the priest shall inquire of the couple which form of the vows they have agreed to use.
The couple may read the vows (sections 9–16) or repeat them after the priest.

Prayers Instead of the additional prayers (sections 31–38, pages xxii–xxiv), prayers which the couple have written or selected in co-operation with the priest may be used. Silence may be kept; or free prayer may be offered.

Congregational Prayers Sections 32, 33, 36, and 38 (pages xxii–xxiv) may be said by the congregation if so desired.

V. G

Praise, my soul, the king of heaven   1

Words: from Psalm 103
H F Lyte (1793–1847)
Music: J Goss (1800–1880)
Descant: Robin Sheldon

Praise my soul   8 7 8 7 8 7

Verses 2, 3 and 4 overleaf

Harmony

2 Praise him for his grace and fa - vour to his peo - ple

in dis - tress; praise him still the same as ev - er,

slow to blame and swift to bless: Al - le - lu - ia,

al - le - lu - ia! glo - rious in his faith - ful - ness!

Verse 4 overleaf

At the Introduction

Descant

4 An - gels, help us____ to a dore____
him ____ you be - hold____ him face____ to ____ face;
sun and moon,____ bow____ down be - fore____ him —

4 An - gels, help us to a - dore
him — you be - hold him face to face;
sun and moon, bow down be - fore him —

2   # All creatures of our God and King

Easter Song (Lasst uns erfreuen)
8 8 4 4 8 8 and Alleluias

Words: after Francis of Assisi (1182–1226)
W H Draper (1855–1933)
in this version Jubilate Hymns
Music: *Geistliche Kirchengesang* Cologne 1623
arranged Noël Tredinnick

1 All   crea-tures of our God and king,   lift
2 Swift rush-ing wind so wild and strong,   white
3 Cool flow-ing wa-ter, pure and clear,   make

up your voice and with us   sing   Al - le - lu - ia,   al - le -
clouds that sail in heaven a - long,   O__ praise him, al - le -
mu - sic for your Lord to hear: Al - le - lu - ia,   al - le -

- lu - ia!   Bright   burn - ing sun with gol - den
- lu - ia!   New   ris - ing dawn in praise re -
- lu - ia!   Fierce   fire so mas - ter - ful and

beam,   soft   shin-ing moon with   sil - ver   gleam,
- joice,   you   lights of eve - ning find   a   voice;   O___
bright   giv - ing to   us   both warmth and   light,

praise   him,   O___   praise   him,   Al - le - lu - i-a,   al - le -

- lu - ia,   al - le - lu   -   ia!

4 People and nations, take your part,
   love and forgive with all your heart.
      Alleluia, alleluia!
   All who long pain and sorrow bear,
   trust God and cast on him your care;
      O praise him . . .

5 Let all things their creator bless
   and worship him in lowliness:
      Alleluia, alleluia!
   Praise, praise the Father, praise the Son,
   and praise the Spirit, Three-in-One,
      O praise him . . .

3

Christ is made the sure foundation

Words: from the Latin (c seventh century)
J M Neale (1818–1866)
in this version Jubilate Hymns
Music: H Purcell (1659–1695)
Descant: James Gillespie

Westminster Abbey   8 7 8 7 8 7

5 Praise   and   hon - our   to____   the   Fa - ther,

1 Christ   is   made   the   sure   foun - da - tion,
2 All   with - in   that   ho - ly   ci - ty
3 We   as   liv - ing   stones   im - plore   you:
4 Here   en - trust   to   all   your   ser - vants
5 Praise   and   hon - our   to   the   Fa - ther,

praise   and   hon - our   to   the____   Son,   praise   and

Christ   the   head____   and   cor - ner - stone   cho - sen
dear - ly   loved____   of   God   on   high,   in   ex -
Come   a - mong____   us,   Lord,   to   day!   With   your
what   we   long____   from   you   to   gain —   that   on
praise   and   hon - our   to   the   Son,   praise   and

hon - our to the Spi - rit, ev - er Three____ and

of the Lord and pre - cious, bind - ing all____ the
- ult - ant ju - bi - la - tion sing, in per - fect
gra - cious lov - ing - kind - ness hear your child - ren
earth and in the hea - vens we one peo - ple
hon - our to the Spi - rit, ev - er Three____ and

ev - er____ One; one in power____ and one in

Church in one; ho - ly Zi - on's help for
har - mo - ny; God the One - in - Three a -
as____ we pray; and the ful - ness of your
ev - er One; one in power and one in

glo - ry while e - ter - nal a - ges____ run.

ev - er, and her con - fi - dence a - lone.
- dor - ing in glad hymns e - ter - nal - ly.
bless - ing in our fel - low - ship dis - play.
glo - ry ev - er - more with you we reign.
glo - ry while e - ter - nal a - ges run.

4

Jesus shall reign

nice

I Watts (1674–1748)
in this version Jubilate Hymns
Music: T Williams' *Psalmodia Evangelica* 1789

Truro   8 8 8 8 (LM)

1 Je - sus shall reign where - 'er the sun does
2 Peo - ple and realms of ev - ery tongue de -
3 Bless - ings a - bound where Je - sus reigns — the

his suc - ces - sive_ jour - neys run; his king - dom stretch from
-clare his love_ in_ sweet - est song, and child - ren's voi - ces
pri - soner leaps_ to_ lose his chains, the wea - ry find e -

shore_ to_ shore till moons shall rise and set no more.
shall pro - claim their ear - ly bless - ings on his name.
-ter - nal_ rest, the hun - gry and the poor are blessed.

4 To him shall endless prayer be made,
and princes throng to crown his head;
his name like incense shall arise
with every morning sacrifice.

5 Let all creation rise and bring
the highest honours to our King;
angels descend with songs again
and earth repeat the loud 'Amen!'

Immortal, invisible, God only wise

5

St Denio   11 11 11 11

Words: W C Smith (1824–1908)
in this version Jubilate Hymns
Music: Welsh hymn melody 1839
verse 4 arranged with descant Douglas Guest

1 Im - mor - tal, in - vi - si - ble, God on - ly wise,
2 Un - rest - ing, un - hast - ing, and si - lent as light,
3 To all life you give, Lord, to both great and small,
(4) We wor - ship be - fore you, great Fa - ther of light,

in light in - ac - ces - si - ble hid from our eyes;
nor want - ing nor wast - ing, you rule us in might;
in all life you live, Lord, the true life of all:
while an - gels a - dore you, all veil - ing their sight;

most ho - ly, most glo - rious, the an - cient of days,
your jus - tice like moun - tains high soar - ing a - bove
we blos - som and flour - ish, un - cer - tain and frail;
our prais - es we ren - der, O Fa - ther, to you

al - migh - ty, vic - tor - ious, your great name we praise.
your clouds which are foun - tains of good - ness and love.
we wi - ther and per - ish, but you ne - ver fail.
whom on - ly the splen - dour of light hides from view.

Verse 4 with descant overleaf

our prais - es_____ we_____ ren - der, O

our prais - es we ren - der, O

Fa - ther, to you whom_____ on - ly the

Fa - ther, to you whom on - ly the

splen - dour of_____ light hides from view.

splen - dour of light hides from view.

6(i) Let all the world in every corner sing

Luckington 10 4 6 6 6 6 10 4

Words: G Herbert (1593–1632)
Music: B Harwood (1859–1949)

1 Let all the world in ev-ery cor-ner sing, 'My God and King!'
2 Let all the world in ev-ery cor-ner sing, 'My God and King!'

The heavens are not too high, his praise may thi - ther fly;
The church with psalms must shout — no door can keep them out;

the earth is not too low, his prais - es there may grow:
but a - bove all, the heart must bear the long - est part:

let all the world in ev-ery cor-ner sing, 'My God and King!'

Let all the world in every corner sing   6(ii)

Herbert   10 4 6 6 6 6 10 4

Words: G Herbert (1593–1632)
Music: H A Dyer (1878–1917)

1 Let all the world in ev-ery cor - ner sing, 'My God and King!'
2 Let all the world in ev-ery cor - ner sing, 'My God and King!'

The heavens are not too high,   his praise may thi - ther fly;
The church with psalms must shout —   no door can keep them out;

the earth is not too low,   his prais - es there may grow:
but a - bove all, the heart must bear the long - est part:

let all the world in ev - ery cor - ner sing, 'My God and King!'

7

Stand up and bless the Lord

Carlisle 6 6 8 6 (SM)

Words: J Montgomery (1771–1854)
Music: C Lockhart (1745–1815)
Descant: John Barnard

1 Stand   up   and   bless___ the___ Lord,   you
2 Though high   a - bove___ all___ praise,   a -
3 O   for   the   liv - ing___ flame   from
4 God   is   our   strength   and___ song,   and
(5) Stand   up   and   bless___ the___ Lord,   the

peo - ple___ of   his___ choice;___ stand   up   and___ praise   the___
- bove   all___ bless - ing___ high,   who   would   not___ fear   his___
his   own   al - tar___ brought,   to   touch   our___ lips,   our___
his   sal - va - tion___ ours: then   be   his___ love   in___
Lord   your___ God   a - dore;___ stand   up   and___ praise   his___

Lord   your___ God   with   heart   and___ soul   and   voice.
ho - ly___ name,   give   thanks   and___ glo - ri - fy?
minds   in - spire,   and   wing   to___ heaven   our   thought!
Christ   pro - claimed   with   all   our___ ran - somed   powers.
glo - rious___ name   both   now   and___ ev - er - more.

Descant

5 Stand up and bless the Lord, the

5 Stand up and bless the Lord, the

Lord your God a - dore; stand up and praise his

Lord your God a - dore; stand up and praise his

glo - rious name both now and ev - er - more.

glo - rious name both now and ev - er - more.

8 God is love – his the care

Personent hodie   6 6 6 6 6 5 5 3 9

Words: P Dearmer (1867–1936)
Music: *Piae Cantiones* 1582
arranged G Holst (1874–1934)

Brightly

1 God is love –   his   the   care,
2 Je - sus shared   all   our   pain,
3 To   our Lord   praise we sing –

(Octaves ad lib.)

tend - ing   each,   ev - ery - where;   God   is   love –
lived   and   died,   rose   a - gain,   rules   our   hearts,
light   and   life,   friend   and   king,   com - ing   down

all   is   there!   Je - sus   came   to   show   him,
now   as   then –   for   he   came   to   save   us
love   to   bring,   pat - tern   for   our   du - ty,

that we all might know him:
by the truth he gave us: Sing a - loud,
show - ing God in beau - ty:

loud, loud; sing a - loud, loud, loud:

God is good, God is truth, God is beau - ty — praise him!

9(i)　Holy Spirit, gracious guest

Charity 7 7 7 5

Words: from 1 Corinthians 13
C Wordsworth (1807–1885)
in this version Jubilate Hymns
Music: J Stainer (1840–1901)

1 Ho - ly Spi - rit, gra - cious guest,
2 Faith that moun - tains could re - move,
3 Though I as a mar - tyr bleed,

hear and grant our heart's re - quest___ for that gift su -
tongues of earth or heaven a - bove,___ know - ledge, all things,
give my goods the poor to feed, ___ all is vain if

- preme and best:___ ho - ly heaven - ly love.
emp - ty prove___ if I have no love.
love I need:___ there - fore give me love.

Organ

4 Love is kind and suffers long,
　love is pure and thinks no wrong,
　love than death itself more strong:
　　therefore give us love.

5 Prophecy will fade away,
　melting in the light of day;
　love will ever with us stay:
　　therefore give us love.

6 Faith and hope and love we see
　joining hand in hand agree –
　but the greatest of the three,
　　and the best, is love.

Holy Spirit, gracious guest

Guildford Cathedral 7 7 7 5

Words: from 1 Corinthians 13
C Wordsworth (1807–1885)
in this version Jubilate Hymns
Music: Grayston Ives

1 Holy Spirit, gracious guest, hear and grant our heart's request for that gift supreme and best: holy heavenly love.

2 Faith that mountains could remove, tongues of earth or heaven above, knowledge, all things, empty prove if I have no love.

3 Though I as a martyr bleed, give my goods the poor to feed, all is vain if love I need: therefore give me love.

4 Love is kind and suffers long,
love is pure and thinks no wrong,
love than death itself more strong:
    therefore give us love.

5 Prophecy will fade away,
melting in the light of day;
love will ever with us stay:
    therefore give us love.

6 Faith and hope and love we see
joining hand in hand agree –
but the greatest of the three,
    and the best, is love.

At the Introduction

10(i) Love divine, all loves excelling

Blaenwern 8 7 8 7 D

Words: C Wesley (1707–1788)
in this version Word & Music
Music: W P Rowlands (1860–1937)

1 Love di - vine, all loves___ ex - cell - ing, joy of
3 Come, al - migh - ty to___ de - liv - er, let us
5 Fin - ish then your new___ cre - a - tion: pure and

heaven, to earth___ come down: fix in us your
all your grace___ re - ceive; sud - den - ly re -
spot - less let___ us be; let us see your

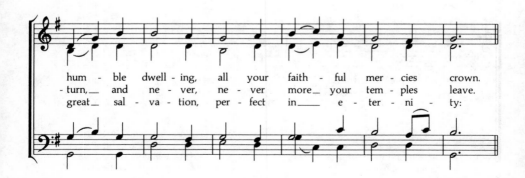

hum - ble dwell - ing, all your faith - ful mer - cies crown.
- turn,___ and ne - ver, ne - ver more___ your tem - ples leave.
great___ sal - va - tion, per - fect in___ e - ter - ni - ty:

2 Je - sus, you__ are all__ com - pas - sion, pure, un -
4 We would al - ways give__ you bless - ing, serve you
6 Changed from glo - ry in - to glo - ry till in

- bound - ed love__ im - part: vi - sit us with
as__ your hosts__ a - bove, pray, and praise you
heaven_ we take__ our place, there to sing sal -

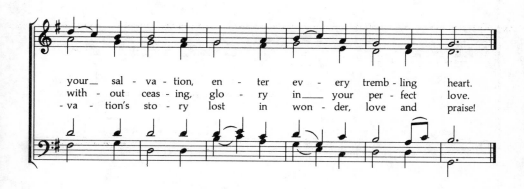

your__ sal - va - tion, en - ter ev - ery tremb - ling heart.
with - out ceas - ing, glo - ry in__ your per - fect love.
- va - tion's sto - ry lost in won - der, love and praise!

10(ii)   Love divine, all loves excelling

Love divine   8 7 8 7

Words: C Wesley (1707–1788)
in this version Word & Music
Music: J Stainer (1840–1901)

Lovely J.G

1 Love di - vine,— all loves ex - cell - ing, joy of
heaven, to earth come down: fix in us— your hum - ble
dwell - ing, all your faith - ful mer - cies crown.

2 Je - sus, you— are all com - pas - sion, pure, un -
bound - ed love im - part: vi - sit us— with your sal -
va - tion, en - ter ev - ery trembl - ing heart.

3 Come, al - migh - ty to de - liv - er, let us
all your grace re - ceive; sud - den - ly— re - turn, and
ne - ver, ne - ver more your tem - ples leave.

4 We would always give you blessing,
serve you as your hosts above,
pray, and praise you without ceasing,
glory in your perfect love.

5 Finish then your new creation:
pure and spotless let us be;
let us see your great salvation,
perfect in eternity:

6 Changed from glory into glory
till in heaven we take our place,
there to sing salvation's story
lost in wonder, love and praise!

The new commandment that I give to you   11

New Commandment

Words: from John 13
Music: Unknown
arranged Norman Warren

The new com-mand-ment that I give to you is to love one an-o-ther as I have loved you; is to love one an-o-ther as I have loved you. By this shall peo-ple know you are my dis-ci-ples— if you have love one for an-o-ther;____ by this shall peo-ple know you are my dis-ci-ples— if you have love one for an-o-ther.____

12(i)

Faith is your gift

Harewood 6 6 6 6 8 8

Words: David Mowbray
Music: S S Wesley (1810–1876)

1 Faith is your gift, Lord God,_ which grasps the_ world un - seen
2 Hope is your gift, Lord God;_ it stands and_ looks a - far
3 Love is your gift, Lord God,_ and while love serves it sings;
4 Christ is your gift, Lord God;_ a - mong the_ poor he came,

and holds it firm, as real as this world's goods have been:
be - yond death's Fri - day gate to Eas - ter's morn - ing star:
re - joic - es in the right, be - lieves and bears all things:
yet mak - ing ma - ny rich who call up - on his name:

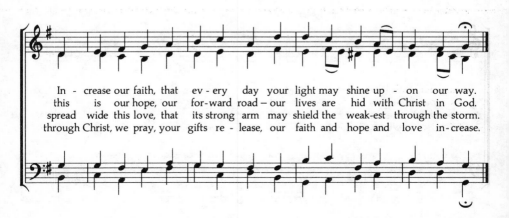

In - crease our faith, that ev - ery day your light may shine up - on our way.
this is our hope, our for-ward road – our lives are hid with Christ in God.
spread wide this love, that its strong arm may shield the weak-est through the storm.
through Christ, we pray, your gifts re - lease, our faith and hope and love in-crease.

Faith is your gift

Christchurch   6 6 6 6 8 8

Words: David Mowbray
Music: C Steggall (1826–1905)

1 Faith   is   your gift, Lord   God,   which grasps the world un - seen   and
2 Hope   is   your gift, Lord   God;   it   stands and looks a - far   be -
3 Love   is   your gift, Lord   God,   and   while love serves it   sings;   re -
4 Christ   is   your gift, Lord   God;   a - mong the poor he   came,   yet

holds   it   firm,   as   real   as   this world's goods have   been: In -
- yond death's Fri - day   gate   to   Eas - ter's morn - ing   star: this
- joic - es   in   the   right,   be - lieves and bears all   things: spread
mak - ing   ma - ny   rich   who   call up - on   his   name: through

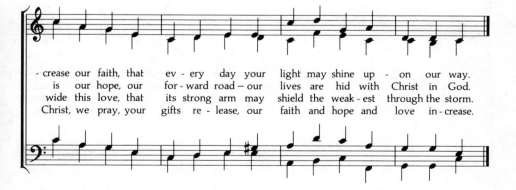

- crease our faith, that   ev - ery   day your   light may shine up - on   our way.
   is   our hope, our   for - ward road – our   lives   are   hid with Christ in God.
wide   this love, that   its strong arm may   shield the weak - est through the storm.
Christ, we pray, your   gifts re - lease, our   faith and hope and   love   in - crease.

13 Jesus, stand among us

Words and music: Graham Kendrick

1&3 Je-sus, stand a-mong us at the meet-ing of our lives, be our sweet a-
2 So to you we're gath-ering out of each and ev-ery land, Christ the love be-

-gree-ment at the meet-ing of our eyes:
-tween us at the join-ing of our hands: O Je-sus, we love you,

so we ga-ther here — join our hearts in u-ni-ty, and

take a-way our fear. our fear.

Words and music: © 1977 Make Way Music / Thankyou Music,
PO Box 75, Eastbourne, East Sussex BN23 6NW

Surprised by joy no song can tell

Melcombe   8 8 8 8 (LM)

Words: Erik Routley (1917–1982)
Music: S Webbe the elder (1740–1816)

1 Sur - prised by joy no song can tell, no
2 Be - yond an an - gel's mind is this, best
3 Faith, hope and love here come a - live; God's

thought can com - pass, here we stand to ce - le - brate e -
gift, a - lone to mor - tals given; the love of par - ent,
ve - ry be - ing is made known, when giv - ing and for -

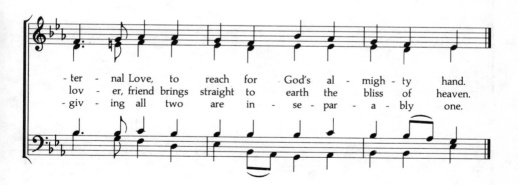

-ter - nal Love, to reach for God's al - migh - ty hand.
lov - er, friend brings straight to earth the bliss of heaven.
-giv - ing all two are in - se - par - a - bly one.

4 For all this splendour, all this joy
  is ours because a Father's care —
  large, generous, patient, strong as death —
  showed us in Christ what love can dare.

5 Your banner over us be love,
  your grace refresh our travelling days,
  your power sustain, your beauty cheer,
  our words, our home, our lives be praise!

15   O God beyond all praising

Thaxted   13 13 13 13 13 13

Words: Michael Perry
Music: G Holst (1874–1934)

1 O___ God be-yond all prais-ing, we wor-ship you to -
2 Then__ hear, O gra-cious Sav-iour, ac-cept the love we

- day and__ sing the love a - maz - ing that
bring, that__ we who know your fav - our may

songs can - not re - pay; for__ we can on - ly
serve you as our king; and__ whe - ther our to -

won - der at__ ev - ery gift you send, at__
- mor - rows be__ filled with good or ill, we'll__

bless - ings with - out num - ber and mer - cies with - out
tri - umph through our sor - rows and rise to bless you

end: we___ lift our hearts be - fore___ you and
still: to___ mar - vel at your beau - ty and

wait up - on your word, we___ hon - our and a -
glo - ry in your ways, and___ make a joy - ful

- dore___ you, our great and migh - ty Lord.
du - ty our sac - ri - fice of praise!

16   Sing out in gladness

Christe Sanctorum   11 11 11 5

Words: John E Bowers
Music: Melody from *Paris Antiphoner* 1681
arranged David Iliff
verse 5 arranged with descant John Wilson

1 Sing out in glad - ness; sing in ju - bi - la - tion! Love is the
2 Praise to the Fa - ther, who is Love and lov - ing, bring - ing to -
3 Praise to the Sav - iour, love of God re - veal - ing, here at this
4 Praise to the Spi - rit, love of God im - part - ing, mak - ing two
(5) Praise to the Fa - ther, who is Love and lov - ing; praise to the

theme - song of our ce - le - bra - tion: love of the God - head,
- ge - ther those who stand be - fore him: give now your child - ren
wed - ding with his pro - mised pres - ence: show forth your glo - ry
hearts one, ne - ver to be part - ed: strength - en their weak - ness,
Sav - iour, love of God re - veal - ing; praise to the Spi - rit,

love of bride and bride - groom, love ev - er - last - ing.
joy in one an - o - ther, grant them your bless - ing.
in their lives to - ge - ther, grant them your bless - ing.
light - en a - ny sor - row, grant them your bless - ing.
love of God im - part - ing, praise ev - er - last - ing.

The left hand tenor part in square brackets should if possible be played as a prominent solo.

17   Your love, O God, has called us here

Words: Russell Schulz-Widmar
Music: English traditional melody
collected R Vaughan Williams (1872–1958)
arranged David Iliff

Herongate   8 8 8 8 (LM)

1 Your love, O God, has called us here,
    for all love finds its source in you;
    the per - fect love that casts out fear,
    the love that Christ makes ev - er new.

2 O gra - cious God, you con - sec - rate
    all that is love - ly, good and true:
    bless those who in your pres - ence wait,
    and ev - ery day their love re - new.

3 O God of love, in - spire our life,
    re - veal your will in all we do;
    join ev - ery hus - band, ev - ery wife
    in mu - tual love and love for you.

Where may that love be found 18(i)

St George 6 6 8 6 (SM)

Words: David Mowbray
Music: H J Gauntlett (1805–1876)

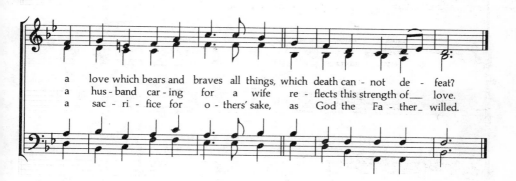

1 Where may that love be found up - lift - ing and com - plete,
2 A par - ent for its child will oft - en moun-tains move;
3 In Christ up - on the Cross Love's depths we see re - vealed;

a love which bears and braves all things, which death can - not de - feat?
a hus - band car - ing for a wife re - flects this strength of___ love.
a sac - ri - fice for o - thers' sake, as God the Fa - ther_ willed.

4 No greater love than this
dare we expect to find,
that seeks the good of the beloved
and leaves self-love behind.

5 Give us, Lord Christ, your help
to tread this narrow way,
to live your resurrection life
and enter into joy.

18(ii)   Where may that love be found

V. nice

Carlisle   6 6 8 6 (SM)

Words: David Mowbray
Music: C Lockhart (1745–1815)
Descant: John Barnard

1 Where may that love be found up -
2 A par - ent for its child will
3 In Christ up - on the Cross Love's
4 No great - er love than this dare
(5) Give us, Lord Christ, your help to

- lift - ing and com - plete, a love which bears and
oft - en moun - tains move; a hus - band car - ing
depths we see re - vealed; a sac - ri - fice for
we ex - pect to find, that seeks the good of
tread this nar - row way, to live your re - sur -

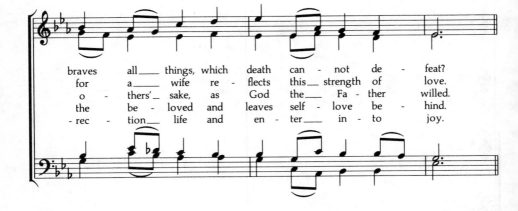

braves all things, which death can - not de - feat?
for a wife re - flects this strength of love.
o - thers' sake, as God the Fa - ther willed.
the be - loved and leaves self - love be - hind.
- rec - tion life and en - ter in - to joy.

Descant

5 Give us, Lord Christ, your help to

5 Give us, Lord Christ, your help to

tread this nar - row way, to live your re - sur -

tread this nar - row way, to live your re - sur -

- rec - tion life and en - ter in - to joy.

- rec - tion life and en - ter in - to joy.

19   Amazing grace

Words: J Newton (1725–1807)
in this version Jubilate Hymns
Music: *Southern Harmony* 1835
arranged John Barnard

Amazing grace   8 6 8 6 (CM)

1 A - maz - ing __ grace — how sweet the sound — that
2 God's grace first __ taught my heart to fear, his
3 Through ev - ery __ dan - ger, trial and snare I

saved a __ wretch like me! __ I once __ was __ lost, but
grace my __ fears re - lieved: __ how pre - cious did that
have al - rea - dy come; __ for grace __ has brought me

now __ am __ found; was blind, but __ now I see. __
grace __ ap - pear the hour I __ first be - lieved! __
safe __ thus __ far, and grace will __ lead me home. __

4 The Lord has promised good to me,
   his word my hope secures;
   my shield and stronghold he shall be
   as long as life endures.

5 And when this earthly life is past,
   and mortal cares shall cease,
   I shall possess with Christ at last
   eternal joy and peace.

For the beauty of the earth

20(i)

England's Lane   7 7 7 7 7 7

Words: F S Pierpont (1835–1917)
Music: English melody
arranged G T Shaw (1879–1943)

1 For the— beau-ty of the earth, for the beau-ty— of the skies,
2 For the— beau-ty of each hour of the day and— of the night,
3 For the— joy of ear and eye, for the heart and mind's de - light,

for the— love which from our birth o - ver and— a - round us lies,
hill and— vale, and tree and flower, sun and moon and stars of light,
for the— mys - tic har-mo - ny link-ing sense to— sound and sight,

Christ our— God, to you we raise this our sac - ri - fice of praise.

4 For the joy of human love,
  brother, sister, parent, child,
  friends on earth and friends above,
  pleasures pure and undefiled,
    Christ our God, to you we raise
    this our sacrifice of praise.

5 For each perfect gift divine
  to our race so freely given,
  joys bestowed by love's design,
  flowers of earth and fruits of heaven,
    Christ our God, to you we raise
    this our sacrifice of praise.

20(ii)   For the beauty of the earth

Ashburton   7 7 7 7 7 7

Words: F S Pierpont (1835–1917)
Music: R Jackson (1840–1914)

1 For the beau-ty of the earth, for the beau-ty
2 For the beau-ty of each hour of the day and
3 For the joy of ear and eye, for the heart and

of the skies, for the love which from our birth
of the night, hill and vale, and tree and flower,
mind's de-light, for the mys-tic har-mo-ny

o-ver and a-round us lies,
sun and moon and stars of light, Christ our God, to
link-ing sense to sound and sight,

you we raise this our sac-ri-fice of praise.

4 For the joy of human love,
brother, sister, parent, child,
friends on earth and friends above,
pleasures pure and undefiled,
    Christ our God, to you we raise
    this our sacrifice of praise.

5 For each perfect gift divine
to our race so freely given,
joys bestowed by love's design,
flowers of earth and fruits of heaven,
    Christ our God, to you we raise
    this our sacrifice of praise.

Morning has broken

Bunessan   10 9 10 9

Words: E Farjeon (1881–1965)
Music: Gaelic melody
arranged Noël Tredinnick

Gently

1 Morn - ing has bro - ken like the first morn - ing;
2 Sweet the rain's new fall, sun - lit from hea - ven,
3 Mine is the sun - light, mine is the morn - ing

black - bird has spo - ken like the first bird:
like the first dew - fall on the first grass:
born of the one light E - den saw play:

praise for the sing - ing, praise for the morn - ing,
praise for the sweet - ness of the wet gar - den,
praise with e - la - tion, praise ev - ery morn - ing,

praise from them spring - ing fresh from the word!
sprung in com - plete - ness where his feet pass.
God's re - cre - a - tion of the new day!

Words: from *The Children's Bells*
published by Oxford University Press
© Estate of Eleanor Farjeon /
David Higham Associates Ltd

Music arrangement: © Noël Tredinnick / Jubilate Hymns †

Schol day!

22(i) All things bright and beautiful

All things bright and beautiful   7 6 7 6 and refrain

Words: C F Alexander (1818–1895)
Music: W H Monk (1823–1889)

All things bright and beau - ti-ful, all crea - tures great and small,

Fine

all things wise and won - der-ful — the Lord God made them all.

1 Each lit - tle flower that o — pens, each lit - tle bird that sings —
2 The pur - ple-head - ed moun - tain, the ri - ver run - ning by,
3 The cold wind in the win - ter, the plea - sant sum - mer sun,
4 He gave us eyes to see them, and lips that we might tell

D.C.

he made their glow-ing col - ours, he made their ti - ny wings.
the sun - set, and the morn - ing that bright-ens up the sky:
the ripe fruits in the gar - den — he made them ev - ery one.
how great is God al - migh - ty, who has made all things well!

All things bright and beautiful

22(ii)

Royal Oak   7 6 7 6 and refrain

Words: C F Alexander (1818–1895)
Music: English traditional melody
seventeenth century
arranged Norman Warren

Unison

All things bright and beau-ti-ful, all crea-tures great and_ small,

all things wise and won-der-ful— the Lord God made them all.

Fine

1 Each lit-tle flower that o-pens, each lit-tle bird that sings — he___
2 The pur-ple-head-ed_ moun-tain, the ri-ver run-ning by, the___
3 The cold wind in the_ win-ter, the plea-sant sum-mer sun, the___
4 He gave us eyes to_ see them, and lips that we might tell how_

D.C.

made their glow-ing_ col-ours, he_ made their ti-ny_ wings.
sun-set, and the_ morn-ing that_ bright-ens up the_ sky:
ripe fruits in the_ gar-den— he_ made them ev-ery_ one.
great is God al-migh-ty, who has made all things well!

23   Great is your faithfulness

Great is thy faithfulness
11 10 11 10 and refrain

Words: T O Chisholm (1866–1960)
in this version Jubilate Hymns
Music: W M Runyan (1870–1957)

1 Great is your faith - ful - ness, O God my Fa - ther,
2 Sum - mer and win - ter, and spring - time and har - vest,
3 Par - don for sin, and a peace ev - er - last - ing,

you have ful - filled all your pro - mise to me;
sun, moon and stars in their cours - es a - bove
your liv - ing pre - sence to cheer and to guide;

you ne - ver fail and your love is un - chang - ing —
join with all na - ture in e - lo - quent wit - ness
strength for to - day, and bright hope for to - mor - row —

all you have been you for ev - er will be.
to your great faith - ful - ness, mer - cy and love.
these are the bless - ings your love will pro - vide.

Great is your faith - ful-ness, great is your faith - ful-ness,

morn - ing by morn - ing new mer - cies I see;

all I have need - ed your hand has pro - vid - ed —

great is your faith - ful - ness, Fa - ther, to me!

24

Jesus is Lord

Words and music: David Mansell

1 Je - sus is Lord! Cre - a - tion's voice pro - claims it,
2 Je - sus is Lord! Yet from his throne e - ter - nal
3 Je - sus is Lord! O'er sin the migh - ty con - queror;

for by his power each tree and flower was planned and made.
in flesh he came to die in pain on Cal - vary's tree.
from death he rose, and all his foes shall own his name.

Je - sus is Lord! The u - ni - verse de - clares it—
Je - sus is Lord! From him all life pro - ceed - ing—
Je - sus is Lord! God sent his Ho - ly Spi - rit

sun, moon and stars in hea - ven cry: 'Je - sus is Lord!'
yet gave his life a ran - som thus set - ting us free.
to show by works of pow - er that Je - sus is Lord.

Chorus

Je - sus is Lord, Je - sus is Lord!

Praise him with al - le - lu - ias, for Je - sus is Lord!

25(i) Jesus, come! for we invite you

Unser Herrscher 8 7 8 7 8 7

Words: from John 2
Christopher Idle
Music: J Neander (1650–1680)
Descant John Barnard

1 Je - sus, come! for we in - vite you, guest and__ mas - ter,
2 Je - sus, come! trans - form our plea - sures, guide us__ in - to
3 Je - sus, come in new cre - a - tion, heaven brought near in
(4) Je - sus, come! sur - prise our dull - ness, make us__ will - ing

friend and Lord; now, as once at Ca - na's wed - ding,
paths un - known; bring your gifts, com - mand your ser - vants,
power di - vine; give your un - ex - pect - ed glo - ry
to re - ceive more than we can yet i - ma - gine,

speak, and__ let us hear your word: lead us through our
let us__ trust in you a - lone: though your hand may
chang - ing__ wa - ter in - to wine: rouse the faith of
all the__ best you have to give: let us find your

need or doubt - ing, hope be born and joy re - stored.
work in sec - ret, all shall see what you have done.
your dis - ci - ples — come, our first and great - est Sign!
hid - den rich - es, taste your love, be - lieve, and live!

Descant

4 Je - sus, come! sur - prise our __ dull - ness, make us will - ing __ to re - ceive

Melody

4 Je - sus, come! sur - prise our dull - ness, make us __ will - ing to re - ceive

more than we can yet i - ma - gine, all the best __ you __ have to give:

more than we can yet i - ma - gine, all the __ best you have to give:

let us find your hid - den rich - es, taste __ your __ love, be - lieve, and live!

let us find your hid - den rich - es, taste your love, be - lieve, and live!

25(ii) Jesus, come! for we invite you

Words: from John 2
Christopher Idle
Music: H Purcell (1659–1695)
Descant James Gillespie

Westminster Abbey 8 7 8 7 8 7

1 Je - sus, come! for we in - vite you, guest and mas - ter,
2 Je - sus, come! trans - form our plea - sures, guide us in - to
3 Je - sus, come in new cre - a - tion, heaven brought near in

friend and Lord; now, as once at Ca - na's wed - ding,
paths un - known; bring your gifts, com - mand your ser - vants,
power di - vine; give your un - ex - pect - ed glo - ry

speak, and let us hear your word: lead us through our
let us trust in you a - lone: though your hand may
chang - ing wa - ter in - to wine: rouse the faith of

need or doubt - ing, hope be born and joy re - stored.
work in sec - ret, all shall see what you have done.
your dis - ci - ples — come, our first and great - est Sign!

Descant

4 Je - sus, come! sur - prise___ our dull - ness, make us will - ing

4 Je - sus, come! sur - prise our dull - ness, make us will - ing

to re - ceive more than we___ can yet i - ma - gine,

to re - ceive more than we can yet i - ma - gine,

all the best___ you have to___ give: let us find___ your

all the best___ you have to give: let us find your

hid - den rich - es, taste your love,___ be - lieve,_ and___ live!

hid - den rich - es, taste your love, be - lieve, and live!

25(iii)   Jesus, come! for we invite you

Oriel 8 7 8 7 8 7

Words: from John 2, Christopher Idle
Music: C Ett's *Cantica Sacra* Munich 1840
arranged W H Monk (1823–1889)
Descant A Gray (1855–1935)

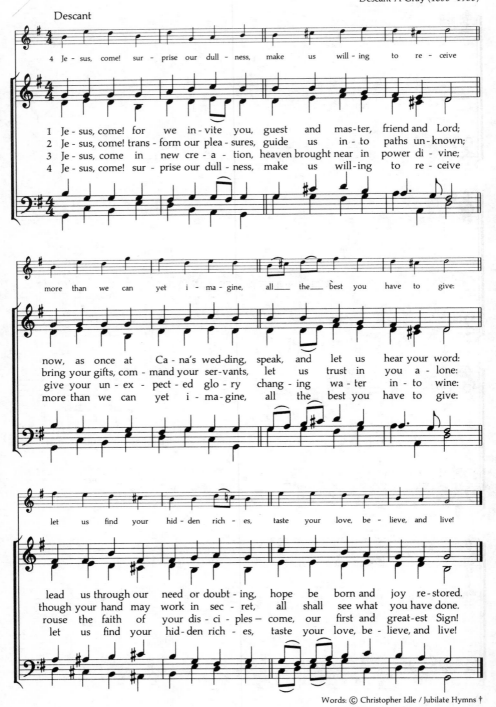

Descant

4 Je - sus, come! sur - prise our dull - ness, make us will - ing to re - ceive

1 Je - sus, come! for we in - vite you, guest and mas - ter, friend and Lord;
2 Je - sus, come! trans - form our plea - sures, guide us in - to paths un - known;
3 Je - sus, come in new cre - a - tion, heaven brought near in power di - vine;
4 Je - sus, come! sur - prise our dull - ness, make us will - ing to re - ceive

more than we can yet i - ma - gine, all the__ best you have to give:

now, as once at Ca - na's wed-ding, speak, and let us hear your word:
bring your gifts, com - mand your ser-vants, let us trust in you a - lone:
give your un - ex - pect - ed glo - ry chang - ing wa - ter in - to wine:
more than we can yet i - ma-gine, all the best you have to give:

let us find your hid - den rich - es, taste your love, be - lieve, and live!

lead us through our need or doubt - ing, hope be born and joy re-stored.
though your hand may work in sec - ret, all shall see what you have done.
rouse the faith of your dis - ci - ples — come, our first and great-est Sign!
let us find your hid - den rich - es, taste your love, be - lieve, and live!

Jesus at a wedding

Jesus, come! for we invite you 25(iv)

Kinessburn 8 7 8 7 8 7

Words: from John 2
Christopher Idle
Music: Norman Warren

26   Jesus, Lord, we pray

Arnstadt   5 5 8 8 5 5

Words: Basil E Bridge
Music: Melody A Drese (1620–1701)

1   Je - sus, Lord,   we   pray,   be   our guest   to -   day!
2   Lord of love   and   life,   bless-ing man   and   wife:
3   Lord of hope   and   faith,   faith - ful un -   to   death:

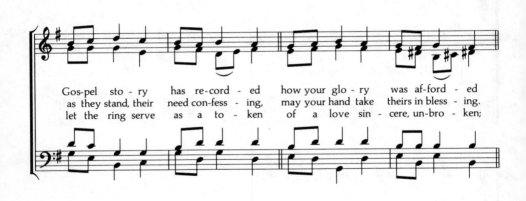

Gos-pel sto - ry   has re-cord - ed   how your glo - ry   was af-ford - ed
as they stand, their   need con-fess - ing,   may your hand take   theirs in bless - ing.
let the ring serve   as a to - ken   of a love sin - cere, un-bro - ken;

to   a   wed - ding   day: be   our guest,   we   pray.
You will share their   life: bless this man   and   wife.
love more strong than   death –   Lord   of hope   and   faith!

To Cana's wedding feast

Laudes Domini 6 6 6 D

Words: David Mowbray
Music: J Barnby (1838–1896)

1 To Ca-na's wed-ding feast___ there comes a wel-come guest,
2 Christ comes, as we re-joice,___ as part-ners make their choice
3 'In sick-ness and in health,___ in po-ver-ty and wealth,

the cou-ple's tru-est friend; then does God's glo-ry shine —
and kneel in church to pray; Christ comes to speak his word —
till death shall part at length': to keep this sol-emn vow

the wa-ter changed to wine by Christ, for whom they send.
more joy-ful ne-ver heard: 'God joins your lives to-day'.
may they dis-co-ver now God's in-ner grace and strength.

4 One flesh, one mutual joy,
one holy mystery,
reflecting Christ's own love;
one home secure and strong
and crowned with children's song,
a gift from God above.

5 With reverence we acclaim
the splendour of God's name,
the glorious Trinity:
may we who worship, know
as on our way we go
the Christ of Galilee!

At the marriage

28(i) The king of love my shepherd is
PSALM

The Followers   8 7 8 7

Words: from Psalm 23
H W Baker (1821–1877)
in this version Jubilate Hymns
Music: The Followers
arranged Norman Warren
Descants: Ivor Keys

Descant 1 is for part of the congregation to sing throughout.
Descant 2 is for choir or instrument in verses 3 and 6.

noth - ing lack if I am his and
where the fer - tile pas - tures grow, with
on his shoul - der gen - tly laid, and

on his shoul - der gen - tly laid, and
Shep - herd, may I sing your praise with -

noth - ing lack if I am his and
where the fer - tile pas - tures grow, with
on his shoul - der gen - tly laid, and

1-5.
he is mine for ev - er. 2 Where ev - er!
food from hea - ven feeds__ me. 3 Per -
home, re - joi - cing, brought__ me. 4 In

home, re - joi - cing, brought__ me. (3 Per -)
- in your house for (6 And) ev - er!

6.

he is mine for ev - er. 2 Where ev - er!
food from hea - ven feeds__ me. 3 Per -
home, re - joi - cing, brought me. 4 In

4 In death's dark vale I fear no ill
with you, dear Lord, beside me;
your rod and staff my comfort still,
your cross before to guide me.

5 You spread a banquet in my sight
of love beyond all knowing:
and O the gladness and delight
from your pure chalice flowing!

6 And so through all the length of days
your goodness fails me never:
Good Shepherd, may I sing your praise
within your house for ever!

At the marriage

28(ii)   The king of love my shepherd is

PSALM

Words: from Psalm 23
H W Baker (1821–1877)
in this version Jubilate Hymns
Music: J B Dykes (1823–1876)

Dominus regit me   8 7 8 7

1 The king of love my shep - herd is, whose
2 Where streams of liv - ing wa - ter flow a
3 Per - verse and fool - ish I have strayed, but

good - ness fails me ne - ver; I noth - ing lack if
ran - somed soul, he leads me; and where the fer - tile
in his love he sought me; and on his shoul - der

I am his and he is mine for ev - er.
pas - tures grow, with food from hea - ven feeds me.
gen - tly laid, and home, re - joi - cing, brought me.

4 In death's dark vale I fear no ill
with you, dear Lord, beside me;
your rod and staff my comfort still,
your cross before to guide me.

5 You spread a banquet in my sight
of love beyond all knowing:
and O the gladness and delight
from your pure chalice flowing!

6 And so through all the length of days
your goodness fails me never:
Good Shepherd, may I sing your praise
within your house for ever!

The Lord's my shepherd   29(i)

PSALM

V. G Better than ii

Words: from Psalm 23
W Whittingham (c1524–1579) and others
Music: J L Macbeth Bain (c1840–1925)
arranged John Barnard

Brother James' Air   8 6 8 6 (CM) extended

1 The Lord's my shep-herd: I'll not want; he makes me down to lie
2 My soul he doth re-store a-gain, and me to walk doth make
3 Yea, though I walk through death's dark vale, yet will I fear no ill;

in pas-tures green: he lead-eth me the qui-et wa-ters by;
with-in the paths of right-eous-ness, e'en for his own name's sake;
for thou art with me, and thy rod and staff me com-fort still;

in pas-tures green: he lead-eth me the qui-et wa-ters by.
with-in the paths of right-eous-ness, e'en for his own name's sake.
for thou art with me, and thy rod and staff me com-fort still.

4 My table thou hast furnishèd
in presence of my foes;
my head with oil thou dost anoint
and my cup overflows,
my head with oil thou dost anoint
and my cup overflows.

5 Goodness and mercy all my life
shall surely follow me;
and in God's house for evermore
my dwelling-place shall be,
and in God's house for evermore
my dwelling-place shall be.

At the marriage

29(ii) The Lord's my shepherd
PSALM

Crimond 8 6 8 6 (CM)

Words: from Psalm 23
W Whittingham (c1524–1579) and others
Music: J S Irvine (1836–1887)
arranged D Grant (1833–1893)
Descant: Paul Edwards

1 The Lord's my shepherd: I'll not want; he
2 My soul he doth restore again, and
3 Yea, though I walk through death's dark vale, yet
4 My table thou hast furnishèd in
(5) Good - ness and mercy all my life shall

makes me down to lie in pastures green: he
me to walk doth make within the paths of
will I fear no ill; for thou art with me,
pre - sence of my foes; my head with oil thou
sure - ly fol - low me; and in God's house for

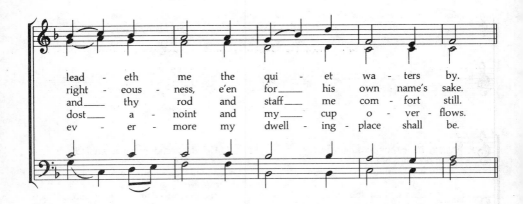

lead - eth me the qui - et wa - ters by.
right - eous - ness, e'en for his own name's sake.
and thy rod and staff me com - fort still.
dost a - noint and my cup o - ver - flows.
ev - er - more my dwell - ing - place shall be.

30 Through all the changing scenes of life

PSALM

Words: from Psalm 34
N Tate (1652–1715)
and N Brady (1659–1726)
in this version Jubilate Hymns
Music: G T Smart (1776–1867)
verse 6 arranged with descant John Barnard

Wiltshire   8 6 8 6 (CM)

1 Through all the chang - ing scenes of life, in
2 O glo - ri - fy the Lord with me, with
3 The hosts of God en - camp a - round the
4 O taste his good - ness, prove his love! Ex -

trou - ble and in joy, the prais - es of my
me ex - alt his name! When in dis - tress, to
dwell - ings of the just; his sav - ing help he
- per - ience will de - cide how blessed are they, and

God shall still my heart and tongue em - ploy.
him I called – he to my res - cue came.
gives to all who in his mer - cy trust.
on - ly they, who in his truth con - fide.

5 Fear him, you saints, and you will then
  have nothing else to fear;
  his service shall be your delight,
  your needs shall be his care.

6 To Father, Son and Spirit, praise!
  To God whom we adore
  be worship, glory, power and love,
  both now and evermore!

Descant

6 To Fa - ther, Son____ and Spi - rit, praise!____ To

6 To Fa - ther, Son___ and Spi - rit, praise!___ To

God____ whom we a - dore be wor - ship, glo - ry,

God whom we___ a - dore___ be wor - ship, glo - ry,

power___ and love,___ both now_____ and ev - er - more!

power and love,__ both now and__ ev - er - more!

31(i) God is our strength and refuge

PSALM

Dam Busters March   7 7 7 5 7 7 11

Words: from Psalm 46
Richard Bewes
Music: E Coates (1886–1958)
arranged John Barnard

1 God is our strength and re-fuge, our pres-ent help in trou-ble;

and we there-fore will not fear, though the earth should change!

Though moun-tains shake and trem-ble, though swirl-ing floods are rag-ing,

God the Lord of hosts is with us ev - er - more!

The Harmony version is harmonically compatible with the Unison setting.

31(ii)   God is our strength and refuge

PSALM

Dam Busters March   7 7 7 5 7 7 11

Words: from Psalm 46
Richard Bewes
Music: E Coates (1886–1958)
arranged Noël Tredinnick

Stately

Introduction

mf   *marcato*   *cresc.*

Verses 1 and 2

1 God   is   our   strength and___ re - fuge,
2 There   is   a   flow - ing___ ri - ver

our   pre - sent   help   in___ trou - ble;   and   we there - fore
with - in   God's   ho - ly___ ci - ty;   God   is   in   the

will   not fear,   though   the   earth___ should   change!
midst   of her –   she   shall   not___ be   moved!

Words: © Richard Bewes / Jubilee Hymns †

Though moun-tains shake and trem-ble, though swirl-ing floods are rag-ing,
God's help is swift-ly giv-en, thrones van-ish at his pres-ence —

God the Lord of hosts is with us ev - er - more!
God the Lord of hosts is with us ev - er -

1.

2.
more!   rit.

Verse 3 slower

3 Come,   see the works of our ma-ker, learn   of his   deeds all - power-ful:

God of mercy, God of grace

PSALM

Heathlands 7 7 7 7 7 7

Words: from Psalm 67 (*Deus misereatur*)
H F Lyte (1793–1847)
Music: H T Smart (1813–1879)

1 God of mer - cy, God of grace, show the bright-ness of your face:
2 Let the peo - ple praise you, Lord! Be by all who live a - dored;
3 Let the peo - ple crown you king! Then shall earth her har - vest bring,

shine up - on us, Sav - iour, shine, fill your church with light di - vine,
let the na - tions shout and sing glo - ry to their sav - iour king,
God to us his bless - ing give, we to God de - vo - ted live;

and your sav - ing health ex - tend to the earth's re - mot - est end.
at your feet their tri - bute pay, and your ho - ly will o - bey.
all be - low and all a - bove, one in joy and light and love.

33(i)   May God be gracious

PSALM

Ellers   10 10 10 10

Words: from Psalm 67 (*Deus misereatur*)
Stephen Horsfall
Music: E J Hopkins (1818–1901)
arranged A S Sullivan (1842–1900)

1 May God be gra - cious, may we see his face;
2 He holds our fu - ture safe with - in his hand;

through - out the wide world may his power be known:
he judg - es right - ly and he guides our ways.

may all the na - tions trust his sav - ing grace,
Earth yields its in - crease — God will bless our land:

and come to wor - ship him be - fore his throne.
may all his peo - ple give him thanks and praise!

May God be gracious

PSALM

33(ii)

Universa laus 10 10 10 10 extended

Words: from Psalm 67 (*Deus misereatur*)
Stephen Horsfall
Music: Anthony Greening

1 May God be gra - cious, may we see his face;
2 He holds our fu - ture safe with - in his hand;

through-out the wide world may his power be known: may all the
he judg - es right - ly and he guides our ways. Earth yields its

na - tions trust his sav - ing grace, and come to wor - ship,___
in - crease — God will bless our land: may all his peo - ple,___

___ and come to wor - ship him___ be - fore his throne.
___ may all his peo - ple give___ him___ thanks and praise!

Original key: D♭

Music: © Anthony Greening

Words: © Stephen Horsfall / Jubilate Hymns †

34(i)
Mercy, blessing, favour, grace
PSALM

Binscombe 7 7 7 7

Words: from Psalm 67 (*Deus misereatur*)
Timothy Dudley-Smith
Music: Alan Davies

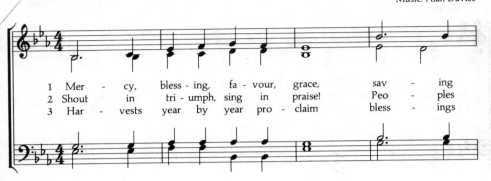

1 Mer - cy, bless - ing, fa - vour, grace, sav - ing
2 Shout in tri - umph, sing in praise! Peo - ples
3 Har - vests year by year pro - claim bless - ings

power to us be shown; bright - ness of the Fa - ther's
all, pro - claim his worth: just and right - eous are his
new in plen - ty poured; all the earth shall fear his

face to the na - tions now be known.
ways, sov - ereign Lord of all the earth.
name, all his peo - ple praise the Lord.

Mercy, blessing, favour, grace 34(ii)
PSALM

Impact 7 7 7 7

Words: from Psalm 67 (*Deus misereatur*)
Timothy Dudley-Smith
Music: David Wilson

Briskly

1 Mer - cy, bless - ing, fa - vour, grace,
2 Shout in tri - umph, sing in praise!
3 Har - vests year by year pro - claim

sav - ing power to us___ be shown; bright - ness of the
Peo - ples all, pro - claim_ his worth: just and right - eous
bless - ings new in plen - ty poured; all the earth shall

Fa - ther's face to the na - tions now be known.
are his ways, sov - ereign Lord of all the earth.
fear his name, all his peo - ple praise the Lord.

At the marriage

34(iii) Mercy, blessing, favour, grace
PSALM

Urchfont 7 7 7 7

Words: from Psalm 67 (*Deus misereatur*)
Timothy Dudley-Smith
Music: John Barnard

Unison

1 Mer - cy, bless - ing, fa - vour, grace,
2 Shout in tri - umph, sing in praise!
3 Har - vests year by year pro - claim

sav - ing power to us be shown; bright - ness of the
Peo - ples all, pro - claim his worth: just and right - eous
bless - ings new in plen - ty poured; all the earth shall

Fa - ther's face to the na - tions now be known.
are his ways, sov - ereign Lord of all the earth.
fear his name, all his peo - ple praise the Lord.

How lovely is your dwelling-place   35(i)

PSALM

Hampton Hill   8 4 8 8 4 4

Words: from Psalm 84
Barbara Woollett
Music: Norman Warren

Gently

Unison

1 How love - ly is___ your_ dwell - ing - place, O Lord   most
2 The spar - row comes to___ build her nest, O Lord   most
3 Your peo - ple come to___ you a - gain, O Lord   most

high, we long to know more of your grace, and yearn to see_ you___
high, and in your house finds peace and rest: so may we too_ be_
high, for here we feel_ your strength, like rain re - fresh - ing us__ through_

face to face, O Lord   most   high,   O Lord   most   high!
ev - er blessed, O Lord   most   high,   O Lord   most   high!
toil and pain, O Lord   most   high,   O Lord   most   high!

4 In fellowship your love we share,
   O Lord most high,
   far better is one day of prayer
   than any spent in worldly care,
   O Lord most high,
   O Lord most high!

5 How lovely is your dwelling-place
   O Lord most high,
   we bring you all our trust and praise,
   and ask your blessing on our days,
   O Lord most high,
   O Lord most high!

At the marriage

35(ii) How lovely is your dwelling-place
PSALM

Melchbourne 8 4 8 8 4

Words: from Psalm 84
Barbara Woollett
Music: Paul Edwards

1 How love - ly is your dwell - ing - place, O Lord most high, we long to know more of your grace, and yearn to see you face to face, O Lord___ most high!

2 The spar - row comes to build her nest, O Lord most high, and in your house finds peace and rest: so may we too be ev - er blessed, O Lord___ most high!

3 Your peo - ple come to you a - gain, O Lord most high, for here we feel your strength, like rain re- -fresh - ing us through toil and pain, O Lord___ most high!

4 In fellowship your love we share,
O Lord most high,
far better is one day of prayer
than any spent in worldly care,
O Lord most high!

5 How lovely is your dwelling-place
O Lord most high,
we bring you all our trust and praise,
and ask your blessing on our days,
O Lord most high!

Sing to God new songs of worship

PSALM

36

Ode to Joy 8 7 8 7 D

Words: from Psalm 98 (*Cantate Domino*)
Michael Baughen
Music: L van Beethoven (1770–1827)

1 Sing to God new songs of wor-ship — all his deeds are mar - vell-ous;
2 Sing to God new songs of wor-ship — earth has seen his vic - to-ry;
3 Sing to God new songs of wor-ship — let the sea now make a noise;

he has brought sal - va - tion to us with his hand and ho - ly arm.
let the lands of earth be joy - ful prais - ing him with thank - ful-ness.
all on earth and in the wa - ters, sound your prais - es to the Lord.

He has shown to all the __ na - tions right - eous-ness and sav - ing power;
Sound up - on the harp his __ prais - es, play to __ him with me - lo - dy;
Let the hills re - joice to - ge - ther, let the __ ri - vers clap their hands,

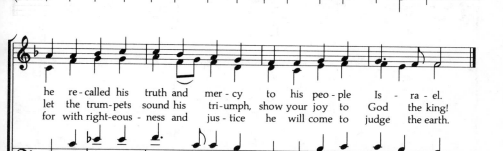

he re - called his truth and mer - cy to his peo - ple Is - ra - el.
let the trum-pets sound his tri-umph, show your joy to God the king!
for with right-eous - ness and jus - tice he will come to judge the earth.

37 O worship the King

PSALM

Words: from Psalm 104
after W Kethe (died 1594), R Grant (1779–1838)
Music: *A Supplement to the New Version* 1708
probably by W Croft (1678–1727)
Descant: A Gray (1855–1935)

Hanover   10 10 11 11

1 O wor-ship the King, all - glo-rious a - bove, and grate-ful-ly
2 O tell of his might and sing of his grace, whose robe is the
3 The earth, with its store of won-ders un - told, Al - migh-ty, your
4 Your boun-ti-ful care what tongue can re - cite? It breathes in the
5 We child-ren of dust are fee - ble and frail — in you we will

sing his power and— his love, our shield and de - fen - der, the
light, whose ca - no - py space; his cha - riots of wrath the deep
power has foun - ded— of old, es - tab - lished it fast by a
air, it shines in— the light, it streams from the hills, it de -
trust, for you ne - ver fail: your mer - cies how ten - der, how

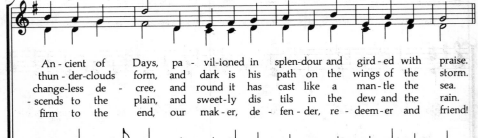

An - cient of Days, pa - vil-ioned in splen-dour and gird - ed with praise.
thun - der-clouds form, and dark is his path on the wings of the storm.
change-less de - cree, and round it has cast like a man - tle the sea.
- scends to the plain, and sweet-ly dis - tils in the dew and the rain.
firm to the end, our mak - er, de - fen - der, re - deem-er and friend!

Verses 3 and 5 may be omitted.

Descant

6 O mea - sure - less Might, un - change - a - ble___ Love, whom an - gels de -

6 O mea - sure - less Might, un - change - a - ble Love, whom an - gels de -

- light to wor - ship___ a - bove: your ran - somed cre - a - tion with___

- light to wor - ship___ a - bove: your ran - somed cre - a - tion with

glo - ry a - blaze, in___ true___ a - dor - a - tion shall sing to___ your praise!

glo - ry a - blaze, in true a - do - ra - tion shall sing to your praise!

38

I will lift up my eyes

PSALM

From Psalm 121
Words and music: Mark Pallant
and Steven Brazier

The accompaniment for verse 1 is also suitable for verses 2 and 3.
The accompaniment may be sung in harmony (alto, tenor and bass) to *Ah*.

Words and music: © 1987 Ears and Eyes,
PO Box TR3, Leeds 12 2PN

slum - ber;___ he who watch - es o - ver

Is - ra - el will nei - ther slum - ber___ nor sleep.

2 The Lord he is your___ guard - ian,___ the
Lord is your de-fence at your right hand;___ the sun will not harm you by
day___ nor the moon___ at night.

3 The Lord will pro - tect you from all dan - ger,___
he will watch o - ver your life;___ the Lord will guard your com-ing and your
go - ing,___ both now___ and for ev - er - more.___

Refrain after verse 3 overleaf

At the marriage

I lift my eyes

PSALM

Davos 9 8 9 7

Words: from Psalm 121
Timothy Dudley-Smith
Music: Michael Baughen and Elisabeth Crocker
SATB version arranged John Barnard

1 I lift my eyes to the qui - et hills in the
2 I lift my eyes to the qui - et hills to a
3 I lift my eyes to the qui - et hills with a
4 I lift my eyes to the qui - et hills and my

press of a bu - sy day; as green hills stand
calm that is mine to share; se - cure and still
prayer as I turn to sleep; by day, by night,
heart to the Fa - ther's throne; in all my ways

in a dus - ty land so God is my strength and stay.
in the Fa - ther's will and kept by the Fa - ther's care.
through the dark and light my Shep - herd will guard his sheep.
to the end of days the Lord will pre - serve his own.

Harmony version overleaf

SOPRANO
I lift my eyes_____ to the qui - et hills_____

ALTO
I lift my eyes to the qui - et__ hills

TENOR
I lift my eyes_____ to the qui - et hills

BASS
I lift my eyes to the qui - et hills

1 in the press of a bu - sy day; as green hills stand__
2 to a calm that is mine to share; se - cure and still___
3 with a prayer as I turn to sleep; by day, by night,__
4 and my heart to the Fa-ther's throne; in all my ways__

1 in the press_ of a bu - sy day;_ as green hills stand
2 to a calm_ that is mine to share; se - cure and still
3 with a prayer as I turn to sleep; by day, by night,
4 and my heart_ to the Fa-ther's throne; in all my ways

1 in the press of a bu - sy day; as__ green hills stand____
2 to a calm that is mine to share; se - cure and still_____
3 with a prayer as I turn to sleep; by__ day, by night,_____
4 and my heart to the Fa-ther's throne; in__ all my ways____

1 in the press of a bu - sy day;_ as green hills stand in a
2 to a calm that is mine to share; se - cure and still in the
3 with a prayer as I turn to sleep; by day, by night, through the
4 and my heart to the Fa-ther's throne; in all my ways to the

Piano or organ accompaniment (compatible with SATB harmony)

40 Unto the hills around me

PSALM

Words: from Psalm 121
J D S Campbell (1845–1914)
in this version Jubilate Hymns
Music: C H Purday (1799–1885)

Sandon   10 4 10 4 10 10

1 Un - to the hills a - round me I lift up my long - ing eyes: whence shall my hope and my sal - va - tion come and whence a - rise? From God the Lord shall come my cer - tain aid, from God the Lord, who heaven and earth has made.

2 Your God will ne - ver let your foot-steps stray, his grasp is sure; he will not sleep, but holds your life in his; you are se - cure: God ne - ver slum - bers; he is al - ways there, and keeps his peo - ple in his ten - der care.

3 God is the Lord, your strong-hold and de - fence, your shield and shade; he will pro - tect by his al - migh - ty power the life he made: no sun shall harm by day, nor moon by night; he is your guard - ian, you are his de - light.

4 From ev - ery e - vil he shall keep your soul, from ev - ery sin; God shall pre - serve your life, your go - ing out, your com - ing in: guard - ing a - bove you, he whom we a - dore will keep you hence - forth and for ev - er - more.

Bless all who trust in God
PSALM

Franconia   6 6 8 6 (SM)

Words: from Psalm 128
David Mowbray
Music: *Harmonischer Liederschatz* (1738)

41(i)

1 Bless   all   who   trust   in   God   and
2 Let   mar - ria - ges   be   strong   and
3 And   since   we   may   not   boast   such

walk   with - in   God's   ways;   bless   ev - ery   soul   whose
spar - kle   bright   as   wine;   let   part - ners   and   let
joys   are   ours   by   right,   teach   us,   good   Lord,   to

hap - pi - ness   springs   from   the   Lord's   own   praise!
child - ren   thrive   and   flou - rish   like   the   vine!
take   your   gifts   with   thanks   and   with   de - light.

41(ii)   Bless all who trust in God
PSALM

Doncaster   6 6 8 6 (SM)

Words: from Psalm 128
David Mowbray
Music: melody by S Wesley (1766–1837)

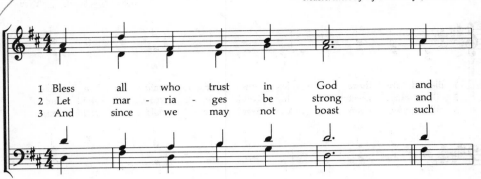

1 Bless all who trust in God and
2 Let mar – ria – ges be strong and
3 And since we may not boast such

walk with – in God's ways; bless ev – ery soul whose
spar – kle bright as wine; let part – ners and let
joys are ours by right, teach us, good Lord, to

hap – pi – ness springs from the Lord's own praise!
child – ren thrive and flou – rish like the vine!
take your gifts with thanks and with de – light.

Blessed are those who fear the Lord   42(i)

PSALM

Culbach 7 7 7 7

Words: from Psalm 128
Christopher Idle
Music: adapted from a chorale in J Scheffler's
Heilige Seelenlust Breslau 1657

1 Blessed are those who fear the Lord, walk - ing in God's
2 Bless - ings greet the hus - band, wife, par - ents, child - ren,
3 Bless us Lord! Your king - dom come; child - ren's child - ren

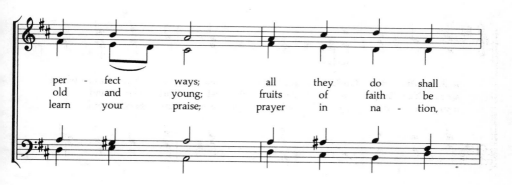

per - fect ways; all they do shall
old and young; fruits of faith be
learn your praise; prayer in na - tion,

bring re - ward, love en - rich - es all their days.
theirs for life, joy in songs to - ge - ther sung.
church and home, peace in Christ to crown our days.

42(ii) Blessed are those who fear the Lord

PSALM

Innocents 7 7 7 7

Words: from Psalm 128
Christopher Idle
Music: *The Parish Choir* 1850

1 Blessed are those who fear the Lord, walk - ing
2 Bless - ings greet the hus - band, wife, par - ents,
3 Bless us Lord! Your king - dom come; child - ren's

in God's per - fect ways; all they do shall bring re -
child - ren, old and young; fruits of faith be theirs for
child - ren learn your praise; prayer in na - tion, church and

- ward, love en - rich - es all their days.
life, joy in songs to - ge - ther sung.
home, peace in Christ to crown our days.

To set their hearts on God

PSALM

Sandys 6 6 8 6 (SM)

Words: from Psalm 128
Christopher Idle
Music: English traditional melody
from W Sandys' *Christmas Carols* 1833

1 To set their hearts on_____ God, to
2 The bride - groom and the_____ bride, the
3 A - round the ta - ble,_____ joy; in

walk in ho - ly ways; in mak - ing such___ a
hus - band and___ the wife, the grow - ing cir - cle
ev - ery room__ be peace; at go - ing out__ and

start as this all bless - ings shall be theirs.
of their home — here is the hap - py life!
com - ing in give love the pride of place.

4 God grant to young and old
   faith's riches, wisdom's health;
   for you and yours, and us and ours,
   long fruitfulness, true wealth.

5 All praises be to God!
   From God all mercies flow:
   all blessings Nazareth once knew
   let every family know!

At the marriage

44(i)

How good a thing it is

PSALM

Venice   6 6 8 6 (SM)

Words: from Psalm 133
J E Seddon (1915–1983)
Music: W Amps (1824–1910)

1 How good a thing it is, how
2 As perfume, by its scent, how breathes
3 And like refreshing dew that
4 God grants the choicest gifts to

plea - sant to be - hold, when all God's peo - ple
fra - grance all a - round, so life it - self will
falls up - on the hills, true u - nion sheds its
those who live in peace; to them such bless - ings

live at one, the law of love up - hold!
sweet - er be where u - ni - ty is found.
gen - tle grace, and deep - er love in - stils.
shall a - bound and ev - er - more in - crease.

How good a thing it is

PSALM

44(ii)

Franconia 6 6 8 6 (SM)

Words: from Psalm 133
J E Seddon (1915–1983)
Music: *Harmonischer Liederschatz* (1738)

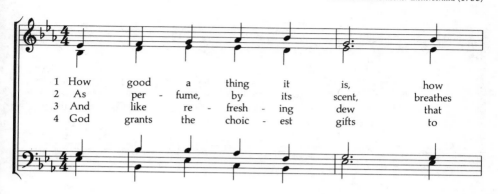

1 How good a thing it is, how
2 As per - fume, by its scent, breathes
3 And like re - fresh - ing dew that
4 God grants the choic - est gifts to

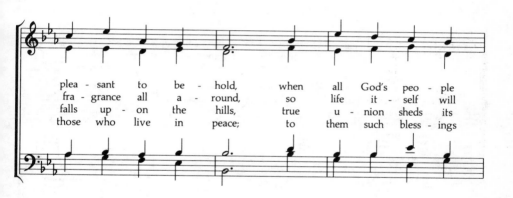

plea - sant to be - hold, when all God's peo - ple
fra - grance all a - round, so life it - self will
falls up - on the hills, true u - nion sheds its
those who live in peace; to them such bless - ings

live at one, the law of love up - hold!
sweet - er be where u - ni - ty is found.
gen - tle grace, and deep - er love in - stils.
shall a - bound and ev - er - more in - crease.

45(i) Jesus the Lord of love and life

Warrington   8 8 8 8 (LM)

Words: J E Seddon (1915–1983)
Music: R Harrison (1748–1810)

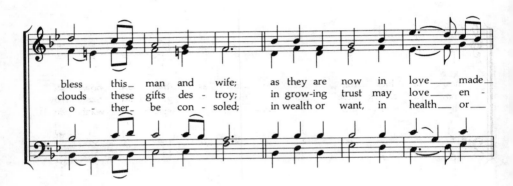

1 Je - sus the Lord of love and life, draw near to
2 Give them each day your peace and joy, let no dark
3 As they have vowed to have and hold, each by the

bless this man and wife; as they are now in love made
clouds these gifts des - troy; in grow-ing trust may love en -
o - ther be con - soled; in wealth or want, in health or

one, let your good will for them be done.
- dure, to keep their mar - riage - bond se - cure.
pain, till death shall part, let love re - main.

4 Deepen, O Lord, their love for you,
  and in that love, their own renew;
  each in the other find delight,
  as lives and interests now unite.

5 Be to them both a guide and friend,
  through all the years their home defend;
  Jesus the Lord of love and life,
  stay near and bless this man and wife.

*The minister may ask the congregation to sit
or kneel in prayer during the singing of
hymns in this section to quiet accompaniment.*

Words: © Mrs M Seddon / Jubilate Hymns †

Jesus the Lord of love and life   45(ii)

Tallis' Canon 8 8 8 8 (LM)

Words: J E Seddon (1915–1983)
Music: T Tallis (c1505–1585)

Quietly

1 Je - sus the Lord of love and life, draw near to bless this man and wife; as they are now in love made one, let your good will for them be done.

2 Give them each day your peace and joy, let no dark clouds these gifts des - troy; in grow - ing trust may love en - dure, to keep their mar - riage - bond se - cure.

3 As they have vowed to have and hold, each by the o - ther be con - soled; in wealth or want, in health or pain, till death shall part, let love re - main.

4 Deepen, O Lord, their love for you,
and in that love, their own renew;
each in the other find delight,
as lives and interests now unite.

5 Be to them both a guide and friend,
through all the years their home defend;
Jesus the Lord of love and life,
stay near and bless this man and wife.

46 Lord Jesus Christ

O perfect love   11 10 11 10

Words: Michael Perry
Music: J Barnby (1838–1896)

Quietly

1 Lord Jesus Christ, in - vit - ed guest and sav - iour,
2 Give them your strength for car - ing and for serv - ing,
3 Be their de - light in joy, their hope in sor - row,

with ten - der mer - cy hear us as we pray;
give them your gra - ces — faith - ful - ness and prayer;
be their true friend in plea - sure as in pain;

grant our de - sire for those who seek your fa - vour,
make their re - solve to fol - low you un - swerv - ing,
guest of to - day and guard - ian of to - mor - row,

come with your love and bless them both to - day.
make their re - ward your peace be - yond com - pare.
turn hum - ble wa - ter in - to wine a - gain!

O perfect Love

O perfect love   11 10 11 10

Words: D F Gurney (1858–1932)
in this version Word & Music
Music: J Barnby (1838–1896)

Quietly

1 O perfect Love, all hu - man thought tran - scend - ing,
2 O perfect Life, be - come their full as - sur - ance
3 Grant them the joy that light - ens earth - ly sor - row,

low - ly we kneel in prayer be - fore your throne,
of ten - der love and stead - fast god - ly faith,
grant them the peace that calms all earth - ly strife;

that you will give the love which knows no end - ing,
of pa - tient hope, and qui - et brave en - dur - ance,
and to life's day the glor - ious bright to - mor - row

to those whom ev - er - more you join in one.
with child - like trust that fears not pain or death.
that dawns up - on e - ter - nal love and life.

48 God be with them

Words: L Tuttiett (1825–1897)
in this version Word & Music
Music: L G Hayne (1836–1883)

Buckland 7 7 7 7

1 God be with them! as they stand heart in heart and hand in hand
2 God be with them! as they go by the path their Lord will show,
3 God be with them! as they share, glad - ly for each o - ther care;

mak - ing first to heaven a - bove vows of faith - ful - ness and love.
each to work with rea - dy will hea ven's pur - pose to ful - fil.
serv - ing Christ in all they do, with af - fec - tion, kind and true.

4 God be with them! as they pray
through a dark and troubled day,
learning then in pain and loss
how to share the Master's cross.

5 God be with them! as they sing
through the joys that life will bring
till they find that deathless love
in the better home above.

Lovely.

May Christ, the Lord of Cana's feast   49

Same music as 72

Repton   8 6 8 8 6 extended

Words: David Mowbray
Music: C H H Parry (1848–1918)

Unison

1 May Christ, the Lord_ of__ Ca - na's feast, who made the wa - ter
2 What God has joined, we__ hear him say, let no - one tear a -
3 What - ev - er joys_ or__ sor - rows come, may stead - fast - ness be
4 With bright - ened eyes_ of__ faith we'll see God's plan for them made

wine, be wel - comed as the hon - oured guest, our
- part! With his two ser - vants here to - day may
theirs! God's truth and kind - ness grace their home, his
plain: so shall our hearts to - ge - ther be up -

ris - en Mas - ter now con - fessed, God's mes - sen - ger_ and_
Christ's own love for ev - er_ stay, true_ bond of mind and_
pre - sence fill the hum - blest room, his_ Spi - rit stir_ their_
- lift - ed in the Tri - ni - ty and_ e - cho the_ A -

sign; God's mes - sen - ger and sign.
heart; true bond of mind and heart.
prayers; his Spi - rit stir their prayers.
- men; and e - cho the A - men.

Before, or during the prayers

50 Praise God, the hour has come

nice music
special

Monks Gate 6 5 6 5 6 6 6 5

Words: David Mowbray
Music: English traditional melody
arranged R Vaughan Williams (1872–1958)

1 Praise God, the hour has come, with joy a-wait-ed;
2 Please God, let dreams not fade, let hope not pe-rish;
3 Pray God, such love will grow stron-ger and deep-er,

two lives are joined in one and de-di-ca-ted:
each lov-ing pro-mise made, help them to che-rish:
that all their guests may know Christ is their keep-er:

their love, from this glad start till death it-self shall part,
in sick-ness and in health, in po-ver-ty or wealth,
so shall the Spi-rit be their guide un-ceas-ing-ly,

with per-se-ver-ing heart shall lead to glo-ry.
in o-ver-com-ing self may they find glo-ry.
their child-ren come to see God's work, God's glo-ry!

Music arrangement: © Oxford University Press

Words: © David Mowbray / Jubilate Hymns †

To God's loving-kindness

51

Oakley 10 9 6 6 10

From Numbers 6
Words and music: Michael Perry
Music arranged Stephen Coates and Norman Warren

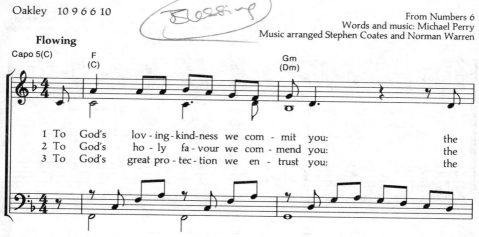

1 To God's lov-ing-kind-ness we com-mit you: the Lord bless your life and make you strong — may the prais-es of God, the Fa-ther and the Son and the Spi-rit — Three-in-One, be your song._____

2 To God's ho-ly fa-vour we com-mend you: the Lord hear your prayers and show his face — and the mer-cy of God, the Fa-ther and the Son and the Spi-rit — Three-in-One, bring you grace._____

3 To God's great pro-tec-tion we en-trust you: the Lord take your hand and give you peace — let the bless-ing of God, the Fa-ther and the Son and the Spi-rit — Three-in-One, ne-ver cease!_____

52   Father, we adore you

Words and music: Terrye Coelho

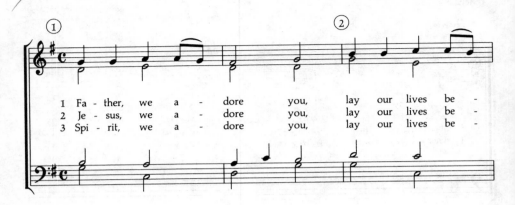

1 Fa - ther, we a - dore you, lay our lives be -
2 Je - sus, we a - dore you, lay our lives be -
3 Spi - rit, we a - dore you, lay our lives be -

- fore you: how we love____ you!
- fore you: how we love____ you!
- fore you: how we love____ you!

This item may be sung as a 3-part round.

Happy are they, they who love God 53

WEDDING VERSION

Binchester   8 6 8 6 (CM)

Words: after C Coffin (1676–1749)
R Bridges (1844–1930)
in this version Word & Music
Music: W Croft (1678–1727)

1 Hap - py   are   they,   they   who   love   God,   whose
2 Glad   is   the   praise,   sweet   are   the   songs,   when
3 Christ   give   their   homes   plea - sure   and   peace   and
4 Then   they   shall   know,   they   who   love   him,   how

hearts   have   Christ   con - fessed;   who   by___   his   cross   have
they   to - ge - ther   sing;   and   strong___   the   prayers   that
make   their   love   his   own;   to - ge - ther   let   them
good   shall   come   from   pain;   and   death___   it - self   can -

found   their   life,   be - neath___   his   hand,   their___   rest.
bow   the   ear   of   heaven's   e - ter - nal___   king.
learn   his   way   and   trust___   his   power   a - lone.
- not   un - bind   their   hap - pi - ness   a - gain.

54 Help us to help each other, Lord

Words: after C Wesley (1707–1788)
in this version Jubilate Hymns
Music: E J Hopkins (1818–1901)

St Hugh 8 6 8 6 (CM)

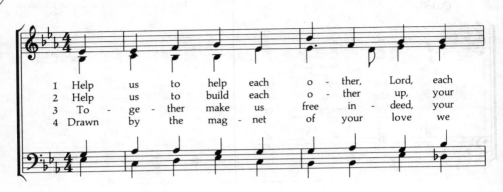

1 Help   us   to   help   each   o - ther,   Lord,   each
2 Help   us   to   build each   o - ther   up,   your
3 To - ge - ther make   us   free   in - deed, your
4 Drawn   by   the   mag - net   of   your   love   we

o - ther's   load   to   bear: that   we   may   live   in
strength with - in   us   prove;   in - crease   our   faith, con -
life   with - in   us   show;   and   in - to   you,   our
find   our   hearts   made   new: near - er   each   o - ther

true   ac - cord,   our   joys   and   pains   to   share.
- firm   our   hope,   and   fill   us   with   your   love.
liv - ing   head,   let   us   in   all   things   grow.
let   us   move,   and   near - er   still   to   you.

May the mind of Christ

WEDDING VERSION

St Leonard's   8 7 8 5

Words: K B Wilkinson (1859–1928)
in this version Word & Music
Music: A C Barham Gould (1891–1953)

Quietly

1 May the mind of Christ our sav - iour
2 May the word of God en - rich us
3 May the peace of God our Fa - ther

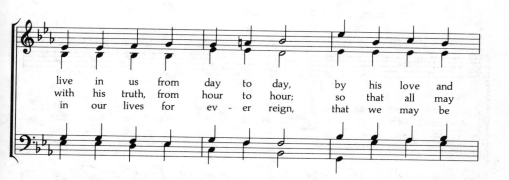

live in us from day to day, by his love and
with his truth, from hour to hour; so that all may
in our lives for ev - er reign, that we may be

power con - troll - ing all__ we do__ and say.
know we tri - umph on - ly through his power.
calm to com - fort those_ in grief_ and pain.

4 May the love of Jesus fill us
as the waters fill the sea,
him exalting, self abasing –
this is victory!

5 May his beauty rest upon us
as we seek to make him known;
so that all may look to Jesus,
seeing him alone.

See other version at 69

56   Eternal Father, Lord of life

Bishopgarth   8 7 8 7 D

Words: H C A Gaunt (1902–1983)
Music: A S Sullivan (1842–1900)

1 Eternal Father, Lord of life, you have in every nation
be-stowed on loving man and wife a share in your creation:
for this you formed the family, the cradle of all living,
and that this wonder still should be to-day we make thanksgiving.

2 Help us to keep our sacred vow of faithfulness, unbroken,
in all our words and works to show each other love unspoken:
grant us your wisdom day by day; through us may grace be flowing,
to help our children on their way, in truth and freedom growing.

3 And when the dangerous days come by of doubt and fear and blindness,
then strengthen every family with courage, faith and kindness;
that we, alert, your love may share alike with friend and stranger,
and be the channels of your care, and draw the sting of danger.

4 May we with joy our tasks fulfil as father, child, or mother,
that families may learn your will in loving one another;
until at last that day may be when all, the truth perceiving,
will know themselves your family, in Jesus Christ believing.

Father hear the prayer we offer

Gott will's machen   8 7 8 7

Words: L M Willis (1824–1908)
Music: J L Steiner (1668–1761)

1 Fa - ther, hear____ the prayer we of - fer:
2 Not for ev - er in green pas - tures
3 Not for ev - er by still wa - ters
4 Be our strength in hours of weak - ness,

not for ease our__ prayer shall be, but for strength that___
do we ask our__ way to be; but the steep and__
would we id - ly__ rest and stay; but would strike the__
in our wand - erings be our guide; through en - dea - vour,__

we may ev - er___ live__ our__ lives cour - age - ous - ly.
rug - ged path - way__ may__ we__ tread re - joic - ing - ly.
liv - ing foun - tains__ from__ the__ rocks a - long our way.
fail - ure, dan - ger,__ Fa - ther,__ be there__ at our side.

58 God of all living

Bunessan   10 9 10 9

Words: Michael J Walker
Music: Gaelic melody
arranged Noël Tredinnick

Gently

1 God of all liv - ing, Fa - ther, we praise you,
2 Per - fect com - pan - ion, God's gift in mar - riage,
3 With love's true splen - dour, Fa - ther de - light us —
4 May there be child - ren, fruit of our lov - ing —

full of thanks - giv - ing for so much love:
one true com - mu - nion, help on life's way:
each giv - ing hon - our, with faith - ful - ness;
true men and wo - men, with faith be - side;

now in this wed - ding, come down a - mong us,
may we be mind - ful in need and plen - ty,
and may the shar - ing of this sweet u - nion
grant us your keep - ing in all our fu - ture,

pour out your bless - ing, hea - ven - ly Dove.
may we be faith - ful ev - ery new day.
deep - en our car - ing, with ten - der - ness.
your love ca - ress - ing, bride - groom and bride.

Happy the home that welcomes you

59

Strength and stay   11 10 11 10

Words: after K P J Spitta (1801–1859)
Honor Mary Thwaites
Music: J B Dykes (1823–1876)

1 Hap - py the home that wel-comes you, Lord Je - sus,
2 Hap - py the home where man and wife to - ge - ther
3 Hap - py the home, O lov - ing friend of child - ren,

tru - est of friends, most hon - oured guest of all;
are of one mind, be - liev - ing in your love;
where they are given to you with hands of prayer;

where hearts and eyes are___ bright with joy to greet you,
through love and pain, pros - pe - ri - ty and hard - ship,
where at your feet they___ ear - ly learn to lis - ten

your slight - est wish - es ea - ger to ful - fil.
through good and e - vil days your care they___ prove.
to your own words and thank you for your___ care.

4 Happy the home
  where work is done to please you,
in tasks both great and small, that you may see
each family doing all as you would wish them
as members of your household, glad and free.

5 Happy the home
  that knows your healing comfort,
where, unforgotten, every joy you share;
until each one, their work on earth completed,
comes to your Father's house to meet you there.

60 Join with us, friends, today

Down Ampney 6 6 11 D

Words: David Mowbray
Music: R Vaughan Williams (1872–1958)
Verse 4 arrangement and descant John Barnard

Verse 1:
1 Join with us, friends, to - day as from our hearts we pray that God him - self may bless our lives to - ge - ther; may he our vows re - ceive, our fal - tering trust for - give and

Verse 2:
2 As Christ the Lord has cared and our ex - ist - ence shared — the joy, the pain, the dark - ness of re - jec - tion: so, as we walk his way, give us each dawn - ing day the

Verse 3:
3 Spi - rit of God, de - scend — pro - mised, un - fail - ing friend — to fash - ion in us gifts be - yond our mak - ing; fruit - ful our branch - es be, root - ed in love — the tree, strong

Verse 4:
(4) Join with us, friends, to - day as from our hearts we pray that God him - self may bless our life to - ge - ther; sing with us joy - ful - ly praise to the Tri - ni - ty, as

help   us   trace   his   im - age   in   each   o -   ther.
power   and   new - ness   of   his   re - sur -   rec -   tion.
through   the   years   to   wea - ther   earth - ly   shak -   ing.
here   in   trust   and   hope   our - selves   we   of -   fer.

Descant

4 Join   with   us,   friends,   to - day

4 Join   with   us,   friends,   to - day

as   from   our   hearts   we   pray   that   God   him - self   may

as   from   our   hearts   we   pray   that   God him - self   may

Take our lives and let them be

WEDDING VERSION

Consecration 7 7 7 7

Words: F R Havergal (1836–1879)
in this version Word & Music
Music: C J Vincent (1852–1934)

Quietly

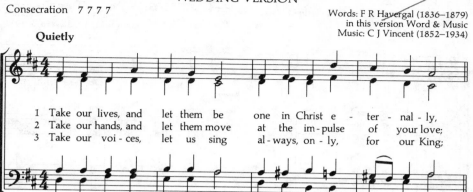

1 Take our lives, and let them be one in Christ e - ter - nal - ly,
2 Take our hands, and let them move at the im - pulse of your love;
3 Take our voi - ces, let us sing al - ways, on - ly, for our King;

take our mo-ments and our days let them flow in cease-less praise.
take our feet, and let them run with the news of vic - tory won.
take our lips, let them pro - claim all the won - der of your name.

4 Take our wealth – all we possess,
 make us rich in holiness;
 take our minds that we may use
 every power as you shall choose.

5 Take our motives and our will,
 all your purpose to fulfil;
 take our hearts – they are your own,
 and shall be your royal throne.

6 Take our love – O Lord, we pour
 at your feet its treasure-store;
 take ourselves that we may be
 yours for all eternity.

See other version at 84

nice

62   Guide me, O my great Redeemer

Cwm Rhondda   8 7 8 7 4 7 extended

Words: after W Williams (1717–1791)
P Williams (1721–1796) and others
Music: J Hughes (1873–1932)

1 Guide me, O my great Redeemer, pilgrim through this barren land; I am weak, but you are mighty — hold me with your powerful hand: Bread of heaven, Bread of heaven, feed me now and evermore (evermore), feed me now and evermore!

2 Open now the crystal fountain where the healing waters flow; let the fiery, cloudy pillar lead me all my journey through: Strong Deliverer, strong Deliverer, ever be my strength and shield (strength and shield), ever be my strength and shield.

3 When I tread the verge of Jordan bid my anxious fears subside; Death of death, and hell's Destruction, land me safe on Canaan's side: Songs of praises, songs of praises, I will ever sing to you (sing to you), I will ever sing to you.

nice

Lead us, heavenly Father, lead us

REVISED VERSION

63

Mannheim 8 7 8 7 8 7

Words: J Edmeston (1791–1867)
in this version Word & Music
Music: F Filitz (1804–1876)

1 Lead us, heaven-ly Fa-ther, lead us through the world's tem-pes-tuous sea; guard us, guide us, keep us, feed us — now and to e-ter-ni-ty, here pos-sess-ing ev-ery bless-ing if our God our Fa-ther be.

2 Sav-iour, heal us and re-store us: all our weak-ness you must know, for you trod this earth be-fore us, felt its keen-est pain and woe; through the drea-ry de-sert, wea-ry and a-lone you chose to go.

3 Spi-rit of our God, de-scend-ing, fill our hearts with heaven-ly joy, love with ev-ery pas-sion blend-ing, plea-sure that can ne-ver cloy: thus pro-vid-ed, par-doned, guid-ed, noth-ing can our peace de-stroy.

See other version at 64

64 Lead us, heavenly Father, lead us
STANDARD VERSION

Mannheim 8 7 8 7 8 7

Words: J Edmeston (1791–1867)
Music: F Filitz (1804–1876)

1 Lead us, heaven-ly Father, lead us o'er the world's tem-pes-tuous sea; guard us, guide us, keep us, feed us — for we have no help but thee, yet pos-sess-ing ev-ery bless-ing if our God our Father be.

2 Sav-iour, breathe for-give-ness o'er us: all our weak-ness thou dost know, thou didst tread this earth be-fore us, thou didst feel its keen-est woe; through the drea-ry de-sert, wea-ry yet o-bed-ient thou didst go.

3 Spi-rit of our God, de-scend-ing, fill our hearts with heaven-ly joy, love with ev-ery pas-sion blend-ing, plea-sure that can ne-ver cloy: thus pro-vid-ed, par-doned, guid-ed, noth-ing can our peace de-stroy.

See other version at 63

Lord Jesus, you have won our hearts

65

Morden 868686

Words: Margaret Clarkson
Music: Norman Warren

Unison

1 Lord Je-sus, you have won_ our hearts and made our lives your own;_
2 Go with us, Sav-iour, through the years with all their paths un - trod;_
3 Teach us to love you as_ we ought, and love each o - ther more_

in this glad hour we hum - bly kneel in prayer be - fore your
far down the fu - ture's hid - den way shines faith's sweet light a -
be - cause we join in love_ to you and prove your mer - cy's

throne:_____ u - nite us now_ in love for you, to
- broad,_____ for come what may,_ one thing we know — the
store;_____ so may we serve_ you here on earth, and

1.2.

live_ for you a - lone!
faith - ful - ness of God!
then_ in heaven a -

3.

- dore!_____

66

Lord of all hopefulness

Words: J Struther (1901–1953)
Music: Irish traditional melody
arranged John Barnard

(handwritten: Lovely)

Slane   10 11 11 12

Quietly

1 Lord of all__ hope - ful - ness,__ Lord of all joy,
2 Lord of all__ ea - ger - ness,__ Lord of all faith,
3 Lord of all__ kind - li - ness,__ Lord of all grace,
4 Lord of all__ gen - tle - ness,__ Lord of all calm,

whose trust, ev - er child - like, no cares could de - stroy:
whose strong hands were skilled at the plane and the lathe:
your_ hands swift to wel - come, your arms to em - brace:
whose voice is con - tent - ment, whose pre - sence is balm:

be there at__ our__ wak - ing, and give us, we pray,
be there at__ our__ la - bours, and give us, we pray,
be there at__ our__ hom - ing, and give us, we pray,
be there at__ our__ sleep - ing, and give us, we pray,

your bliss in our hearts, Lord, at the break of the day.
your strength in our hearts, Lord, at the noon of the day.
your love in our hearts, Lord, at the eve of the day.
your peace in our hearts, Lord, at the end of the day.

Lord of creation

Bunessan 10 9 10 9

Words: David Mowbray
Music: Gaelic melody
arranged Noël Tredinnick

Gently

1 Lord of cre - a - tion, gi - ver of glad - ness,
2 Lord of our past days, life's rich sur - pris - es,
3 Lord of to - mor - row: what will it bring us?
4 Lord, in your keep - ing we are safe al - ways;

in ce - le - bra - tion we come to - day;
clear - ing our path - ways you wise - ly led:
Bless - ing or sor - row, all un - ex - plored:
wak - ing or sleep - ing you watch us still:

loved ones a - round us, hope shin - ing strong - ly,
through pain - ful learn - ing we have moved for - ward,
each si - tu - a - tion calls us to trust you,
save us from los - ing love's pre - cious jew - el,

your love com - plet - ing our deep - est joy.
work - ing and earn - ing our dai - ly bread.
our true sal - va - tion is Christ the Lord.
help us in choos - ing your gra - cious will.

Before, or during the prayers

68   How blessed are those who trust in God

Church Triumphant   8 8 8 8 (LM)

Words: from Psalm 112
Words: Michael Perry
Music: J W Elliott (1833–1915)

1 How blessed are those who trust in God, de -
2 How hap - py those who free - ly give, who
3 How joy - ful those who, strong for truth, re -
4 Then praise the Lord — let joy - ful praise to

- light - ing in his sure com-mand — for rich in grace will
just - ly deal and kind - ly care — for in their dark - ness
- ly up - on the Lord most high; un - like the wick - ed
Fa - ther, Spi - rit, Son be given; to God who loved us,

be their homes, their child - ren migh - ty in the land:
light shall dawn, and long shall be their me - mory here:
they shall live, and lift their heads up to the sky.
came to save and fills our hearts with grace from heaven!

May the mind of Christ

STANDARD VERSION

St Leonard's 8 7 8 5

Words: K B Wilkinson (1859–1928)
in this version Jubilate Hymns
Music: A C Barham Gould (1891–1953)

Quietly

1 May the mind of Christ my sav - iour
2 May the word of God en - rich me
3 May the peace of God my Fa - ther

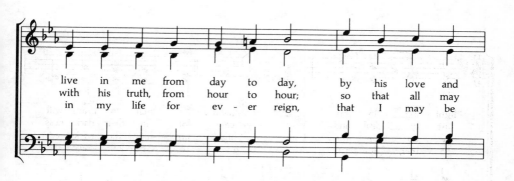

live in me from day to day, by his love and
with his truth, from hour to hour; so that all may
in my life for ev - er reign, that I may be

power con - troll - ing all___ I do___ and say.
see I tri - umph on - ly through his power.
calm to com - fort those_ in grief_ and pain.

4 May the love of Jesus fill me
　　as the waters fill the sea,
　　him exalting, self abasing –
　　　　this is victory!

5 May his beauty rest upon me
　　as I seek to make him known;
　　so that all may look to Jesus,
　　　　seeing him alone.

See wedding version at 55

70   Make me a channel of your peace

St Francis

From the traditional prayer
Words and music: Sebastian Temple
Music arranged Norman Warren

Quietly

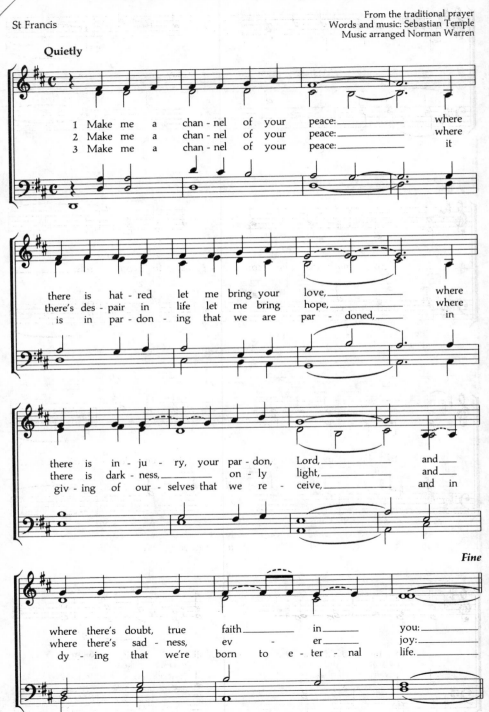

1 Make me a chan-nel of your peace: where
2 Make me a chan-nel of your peace: where
3 Make me a chan-nel of your peace: it

there is hat-red let me bring your love, where
there's des-pair in life let me bring hope, where
is in par-don-ing that we are par-doned, in

there is in-ju-ry, your par-don, Lord, and
there is dark-ness, on-ly light, and
giv-ing of our-selves that we re-ceive, and in

Fine

where there's doubt, true faith in you:
where there's sad-ness, ev-er joy:
dy-ing that we're born to e-ter-nal life.

Chorus

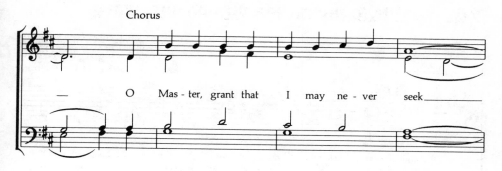

O Mas - ter, grant that I may ne - ver seek_____

so much to be con - soled as to con - sole;_____

to be un - der-stood as to un - der - stand,_____

to be loved, as to love with all my soul!_____

v. nice

71(i) Breathe on me, breath of God

Carlisle   6 6 8 6 (SM)

Words: E Hatch (1835–1889)
in this version Jubilate Hymns
Music: C Lockhart (1745–1815)
verse 4 arranged with descant John Barnard

```
1 Breathe    on    me,   breath   of     God;    fill
2 Breathe    on    me,   breath   of     God,    un -
3 Breathe    on    me,   breath   of     God;    ful -
(4) Breathe  on    me,   breath   of     God:    so
```

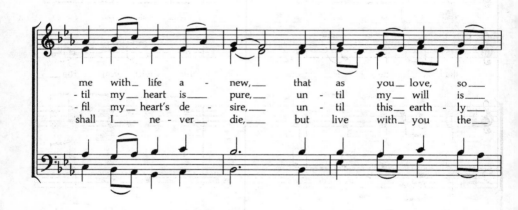

```
  me   with   life   a -  new,    that   as    you   love,  so
- til  my     heart  is   pure,   un -   til   my    will   is
- fil  my     heart's de - sire,  un -   til   this  earth - ly
  shall I     ne - ver    die,    but    live  with  you    the
```

```
  I    may    love,  and   do    what   you   would   do.
  one  with   yours  to    do    and    to    en -    dure.
  part of     me     glows with  your   heaven - ly    fire.
  per - fect   life   of    your  e -    ter - ni -     ty.
```

Descant

4 Breathe on me, breath of God: so

4 Breathe on me, breath of God: so

shall I ne - ver die, but live with you the

shall I ne - ver die, but live with you the

per - fect life of your e - ter - ni - ty.

per - fect life of your e - ter - ni - ty.

71(ii)   Breathe on me, breath of God

Saints Alive

Words: E Hatch (1835–1889)
in this version Jubilate Hymns
Music: Roger Jones

1 Breathe on me, breath of God;___ fill me with life a-new,___ that as you love, so I___ may love, and do what you would do.___

3 Breathe on me, breath of God;___ ful-fil my heart's de-sire,___ un-til this earth-ly part_ of me glows with your heaven-ly fire.___

71(iii) Breathe on me, breath of God

Words: E Hatch (1835–1889)
in this version Jubilate Hymns
Music: R Jackson (1840–1914)

Trentham 6 6 8 6 (SM)

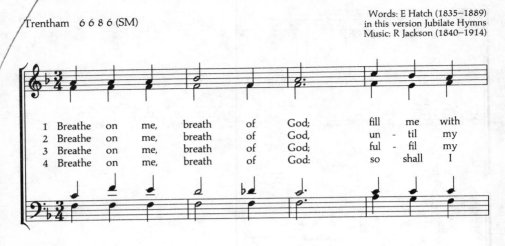

1 Breathe on me, breath of God; fill me with
2 Breathe on me, breath of God, un - til my
3 Breathe on me, breath of God; ful - fil my
4 Breathe on me, breath of God: so shall I

life a - new, that as you love, so
heart is pure, un - til my will is
heart's de - sire, un - til this earth - ly
ne - ver die, but live with you the

I may love, and do____ what you would do.
one with yours to do____ and to en - dure.
part of me glows with____ your heaven - ly fire.
per - fect life of your____ e - ter - ni - ty.

Dear Lord and Father of mankind

72

Repton 8 6 8 8 6 extended

Words: J G Whittier (1807–1892)
in this version Jubilate Hymns
Music: C H H Parry (1848–1918)

Quietly

Unison

1 Dear Lord and Fa - ther_ of man-kind, for - give our fool - ish
2 In sim - ple trust_ like_ theirs who heard, be - side the Sy - rian
3 O sab - bath rest_ by_ Ga - li - lee! O calm of hills a -

ways: re - clothe us in our right - ful mind; in
sea, the gra - cious call - ing of the Lord — let
- bove, when Je - sus shared on bend - ed knee the

pur - er lives your ser - vice_ find, in_ deep - er rev - erence_
us, like them, o - bey his_ word: 'Rise_ up and fol - low_
si - lence of e - ter - ni - ty, in - ter - pret - ed_ by_

praise, in deep - er rev - erence praise.
me, rise up and fol - low me!'
love, in - ter - pret - ed by love!

4 With that deep hush subduing all
our words and works that drown
the tender whisper of your call,
as noiseless let your blessing fall
as fell your manna down,
as fell your manna down.

5 Drop your still dews of quietness,
till all our strivings cease;
take from our souls the strain and stress,
and let our ordered lives confess
the beauty of your peace,
the beauty of your peace.

73   Come down, O Love divine

Words: after Bianco da Siena (died 1434)
R F Littledale (1833–1890)
in this version Jubilate Hymns
Music: R Vaughan Williams (1872–1958)
verse 4 arranged with descant John Barnard

Down Ampney   6 6 11 D

1 Come down, O Love divine!
2 O let it freely burn
3 Let holy charity
(4) And so the yearning strong

Seek out this soul of mine and visit it with
till earth-ly pas-sions turn to dust and ash-es
my out-ward ves-ture be, and low-li-ness be-
with which the soul will long shall far sur-pass the

your own ar-dour glow - ing; O Com-for-ter, draw
in its heat con-sum - ing; and let your glo-rious
-come my in - ner cloth - ing; true low-li-ness of
power of hu-man tell - ing; for none can guess its

near, with - in my heart ap - pear, and
light shine ev - er on my sight, and
heart which takes the hum - bler part, and
grace till we be - come the place in

kin - dle it, your ho - ly flame be - stow - ing.
make my path - way clear, by your il - lum - ing.
for its own short - com - ings weeps with loath - ing.
which the Ho - ly Spi - rit makes his dwell - ing.

Descant

4 And so the yearn - ing strong

4 And so the yearn - ing strong

with which the soul will long shall far sur - pass the

with which the soul will long shall far sur - pass the

O Holy Spirit, breathe on me

N.B: Lovely for choir

O Holy Spirit

Words and music: Norman Warren

Quietly

1 O Ho-ly Spi - rit__ breathe on me,___ O Ho-ly Spi - rit__
2 O Ho-ly Spi - rit__ fill my life,___ O Ho-ly Spi - rit__
3 O Ho-ly Spi - rit__ make me new,___ O Ho-ly Spi - rit__
4 O Ho-ly Spi - rit,__ wind of God,__ O Ho-ly Spi - rit,__

ped.   sim.

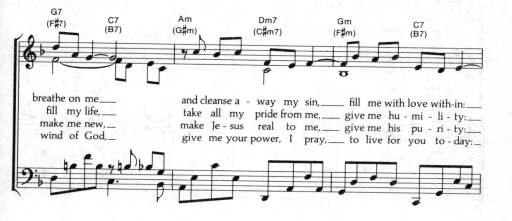

breathe on me___   and cleanse a - way my sin,___ fill me with love with-in:__
fill my life,___   take all my pride from me,__ give me hu - mi - li - ty:__
make me new,__   make Je - sus real to me,__ give me his pu - ri - ty:__
wind of God,_   give me your power, I pray,__ to live for you to - day:__

last time

__ O Ho-ly Spi - rit__ breathe on me!

75 O Lord who came from realms above
WEDDING VERSION

Hereford   8 8 8 8 (LM)

Words: C Wesley (1707–1788)
in this version Word & Music
Music: S S Wesley (1810–1876)

1 O Lord, who came from realms above
2 There let it for your glory burn
3 Jesus, confirm our hearts' desire
4 Here let us prove your perfect will,

and pure celestial fire imparts,
with inextinguishable blaze,
to work and speak and think for you;
our acts of faith and love repeat,

kindle a flame of sacred love
and trembling to its source return
still let us guard the holy fire,
till death your endless mercies seal

upon the altar of our hearts.
in humble prayer and fervent praise.
and still in us your gift renew.
and make the sacrifice complete!

See other version at 76

O thou who camest from above

TRADITIONAL VERSION

Hereford   8 8 8 8 (LM)

Words: C Wesley (1707–1788)
Music: S S Wesley (1810–1876)

1 O thou who camest from above
2 There let it for thy glory burn
3 Jesus, confirm my heart's desire
4 Ready for all thy perfect will,

the pure celestial fire to impart,
within inextinguishable blaze;
to work and speak and think for thee;
my acts of faith and love repeat,

kindle a flame of sacred love
and trembling to its source return,
still let me guard the holy fire,
till death thy endless mercies seal

on the mean altar of my heart.
in humble prayer and fervent praise.
and still stir up thy gift in me:
and make the sacrifice complete.

See wedding version at 75

Before, or during the prayers

77　Spirit of God, unseen as the wind

Skye Boat Song

Words: Margaret Old
Music: Scottish traditional melody
arranged David Peacock

Flowing

Spi - rit of God, un - seen as the wind,
gen - tle as is the dove: teach us the truth and
help us be-lieve, show us the Sav - iour's love!

Fine

1 You spoke to us — long, long a - go — gave us the writ - ten
2 With - out your help we fail our Lord, we can - not live his

word;
way;

we read it still,
we need your power,

need-ing its truth, through it God's voice is heard._____
we need your strength, fol - low-ing Christ each day._____

D.C.

78   Christ is our corner-stone

Words: from the Latin (c seventh century)
J Chandler (1806–1876)
Music: J Darwall (1731–1789)
Verse 4 arranged with descant John Barnard

Darwall's 148th   6 6 6 6 8 8

1 Christ is our cor - ner - stone, on him a - lone we
2 With psalms and hymns of praise this ho - ly place shall
3 Here, gra - cious God, draw near as in your name we
(4) Here may we gain from heaven the grace which we im -

build; with his true saints a - lone the courts of
ring; our voi - ces we will raise, the Three - in -
bow; each true pe - ti - tion hear, ac - cept each
- plore; and may that grace, once given, be with us

heaven are filled; on his great love our
- One to sing; and thus pro - claim in
faith - ful vow; and more and more on
ev - er - more, un - til that day when

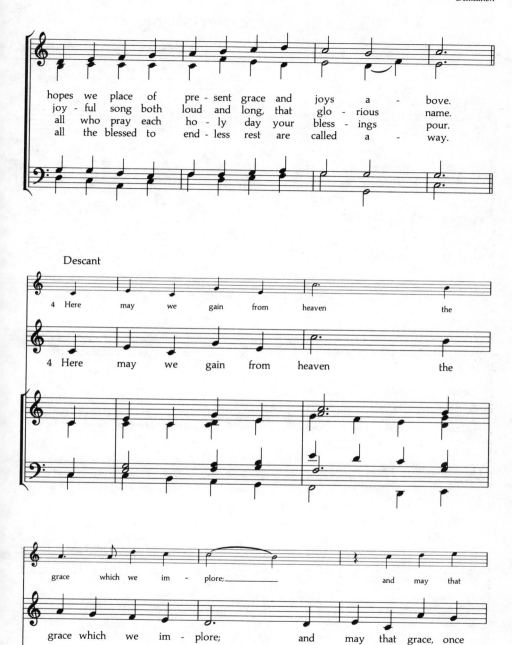

hopes we place of pre - sent grace and joys a - bove.
joy - ful song both loud and long, that glo - rious name.
all who pray each ho - ly day your bless - ings pour.
all the blessed to end - less rest are called a - way.

Descant

4 Here may we gain from heaven the

4 Here may we gain from heaven the

grace which we im - plore;_____ and may that

grace which we im - plore; and may that grace, once

Lord of all power
WEDDING VERSION

Slane   10 11 11 12

Words: J C Winslow (1882–1974)
Music: Irish traditional melody
arranged John Barnard

1 Lord of all power, we give you our will,
in joyful obedience your tasks to fulfil;
your bondage is freedom, your service is song,
and, held in your keeping, our weakness is strong.

2 Lord of all wisdom, we give you our mind;
rich truth that surpasses our knowledge to find,
what eye has not seen and what ear has not heard
is taught by your Spirit and shines from your word.

3 Lord of all bounty, we give you our heart;
we praise and adore you for all you impart —
your love to inspire us, your counsel to guide,
your presence to cheer us, whatever betide.

4 Lord of all being, we give you our all;
for if we disown you we stumble and fall,
but, sworn in glad service your word to obey,
we walk in your freedom to the end of the way.

80

Day by day

Words: after Richard of Chichester
Music: Norman Warren

81 Fill now my life

Richmond 8 6 8 6 (CM)

Words: H Bonar (1808–1889)
Music: adapted from T Haweis (1734–1820)
by S Webbe the younger (1770–1843)
Descant: Norman Warren

1 Fill now my life, O Lord my God, in
2 Not for the lip of praise a - lone, nor
3 Praise in the com - mon things of life, its

ev - ery part with praise: that my whole be - ing
yet the prais - ing heart, I ask, but for a
go - ings out and in; praise in each du - ty

may pro - claim your be - ing and your ways.
life made up of praise in ev - ery part:
and each deed, ex - alt - ed or un - seen.

4 Fill every part of me with praise;
  let all my being speak
  of you and of your love, O Lord,
  poor though I be and weak.

5 Then, Lord, from me you shall receive
  the praise and glory due;
  and so shall I begin on earth
  the song for ever new.

Descant

6 So shall no part of____ day____ or night from

6 So shall no part of day____ or night from

sac - red - ness____ be__ free; but__ all___ my life,___ with

sac - red - ness____ be free; but all___ my life,___ with

you____ my God, in___ fel - low - ship____ shall__ be.

you___ my God, in fel - low - ship____ shall be.

really (wonderful

0 105

82 Lord Jesus Christ, you have come to us
WEDDING VERSION

Living Lord 9 8 8 8 8 3

Words and music: Patrick Appleford
final verse adapted with permission

With strength

Unison

1 Lord Je - sus Christ, you have
Lord Je - sus Christ, now and
2 Lord Je - sus Christ, you have
3 Lord Je - sus Christ, we would

come to us, you are one with us,
ev - ery day teach us how to pray,
come to us, born as one of us,
come to you, live our lives for you,

Ma - ry's son; cleans-ing our souls from
Son of God; you have com - mand - ed
Ma - ry's son; led out to die on
Son of God; all your com-mands we

The italicised verse is sung only at Communion.

all their sin,   pour - ing your love   and good - ness in:
us to do   *this in re - mem - brance, Lord, of you:*
Cal - va - ry,   ris - en from death   to   set us free:
know are true,   your ma - ny gifts   will make us new:

Je - sus, our love for   you we sing —   liv - ing
in - to our lives your   power breaks through — liv - ing
liv - ing Lord Je - sus, help us see   you   are
in - to our lives your   power breaks through — liv - ing

1-3.   **4.**

(Keyboard)

Lord!   Lord!
Lord!
Lord!

Harmony version overleaf

Harmony

1 Lord Je - sus Christ, you have come to us,
Lord Je - sus Christ, now and ev - ery day
2 Lord Je - sus Christ, you have come to us,
3 Lord Je - sus Christ, we would come to you,

you are one with us, Ma - ry's son;
teach us how to pray, Son of God;
born as one of us, Ma - ry's son;
live our lives for you, Son of God;

cleans-ing our souls from all their sin, pour-ing your love and good-ness in:
you have com - mand - ed us to do this in re - mem - brance, Lord, of you:
led out to die on Cal - va - ry, ris - en from death to set us free:
all your com-mands we know are true, your ma - ny gifts will make us new:

Je - sus, our love for you we sing — liv - ing Lord!
in - to our lives your power breaks through — liv - ing Lord!
liv - ing Lord Je - sus, help us see you are Lord!
in - to our lives your power breaks through — liv - ing Lord!

This version is harmonically compatible with the unison setting.

The italicised verse is sung only at Communion.

All for Jesus

All for Jesus   8 7 8 7

Words: W J Sparrow-Simpson (1859–1952)
in this version Jubilate Hymns
Music: J Stainer (1840–1901)

1 All for Je - sus, all for Je - sus!
2 All for Je - sus: you will give us
3 All for Je - sus — you have loved us,

This our song shall ev - er be: you our on - ly
strength to serve you hour by hour; none can move us
all for Je - sus — you have died, all for Je - sus —

hope, our sav - iour, yours the love that sets us free!
from your pre - sence while we trust your grace and power.
you are with us; all for Je - sus cru - ci - fied.

4 All for Jesus, all for Jesus,
   all our talents and our powers,
   all our thoughts and words and actions,
   all our passing days and hours.

5 All for Jesus, all for Jesus!
   This the church's song shall be
   till at last her children gather,
   one in him eternally.

84(i) Take my life and let it be
REVISED VERSION

Nottingham 7 7 7 7

Words: F R Havergal (1836–1879)
in this version Jubilate Hymns
Music: W A Mozart (1756–1791)

Quietly

1 Take my life and let it be all your purpose, Lord, for me; consecrate my passing days, let them flow in ceaseless praise.

2 Take my hands, and let them move at the impulse of your love; take my feet, and let them run with the news of victory won.

3 Take my voice, and let me sing always, only, for my King; take my lips, let them proclaim all the beauty of your name.

4 Take my wealth – all I possess,
make me rich in faithfulness;
take my mind that I may use
every power as you shall choose.

5 Take my motives and my will,
all your purpose to fulfil;
take my heart – it is your own,
it shall be your royal throne.

6 Take my love – my Lord, I pour
at your feet its treasure-store;
take myself, and I will be
yours for all eternity.

See wedding version at 61

Take my life and let it be

REVISED VERSION

84(ii)

Lübeck 7 7 7 7

Words: F R Havergal (1836–1879)
in this version Jubilate Hymns
Music: J Freylinghausen's
Geistreiches Gesangbuch 1704

Quietly

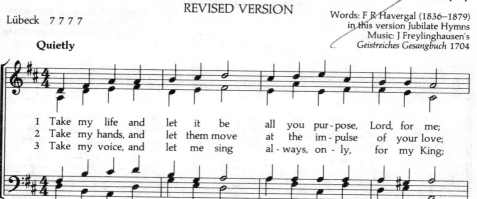

1 Take my life and let it be all you pur-pose, Lord, for me;
2 Take my hands, and let them move at the im-pulse of your love;
3 Take my voice, and let me sing al - ways, on - ly, for my King;

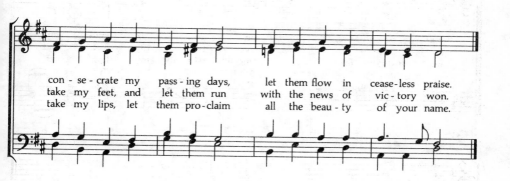

con - se - crate my pass - ing days, let them flow in cease-less praise.
take my feet, and let them run with the news of vic - tory won.
take my lips, let them pro-claim all the beau - ty of your name.

4 Take my wealth — all I possess,
   make me rich in faithfulness;
   take my mind that I may use
   every power as you shall choose.

5 Take my motives and my will,
   all your purpose to fulfil;
   take my heart — it is your own,
   it shall be your royal throne.

6 Take my love — my Lord, I pour
   at your feet its treasure-store;
   take myself, and I will be
   yours for all eternity.

See wedding version at 61

84(iii)
Take my life and let it be
REVISED VERSION

Emma 7 7 7 7

Words: F R Havergal (1836–1879)
in this version Jubilate Hymns
Music: Paul Wright

1 Take   my   life and   let   it   be   all   you pur - pose,
2 Take   my   hands, and   let   them move   at   the im - pulse
3 Take   my   voice, and   let   me   sing   al - ways, on - ly,
4 Take   my   wealth — all   I   pos - sess,   make   me rich   in

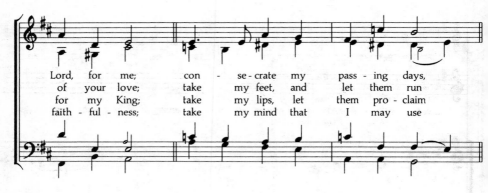

Lord,   for   me;   con   -   se - crate   my   pass - ing   days,
of   your   love;   take   my   feet,   and   let   them   run
for   my   King;   take   my   lips,   let   them   pro - claim
faith - ful - ness;   take   my   mind   that   I   may   use

let   them flow   in   cease   -   less   praise.
with   the   news   of   vic   -   tory   won.
all   the   beau - ty   of   your   name.
ev - ery power   as   you   shall   choose.

5 Take my motives and my will,
all your purpose to fulfil;
take my heart — it is your own,
it shall be your royal throne.

6 Take my love — my Lord, I pour
at your feet its treasure-store;
take myself, and I will be
yours for all eternity.

See wedding version at 61

Descant

6 Take my love — my Lord, I pour at your

6 Take my love — my Lord, I pour at your feet its

feet its trea-sure-store; take my-self, take my-self, and I will

trea-sure-store; take my-self, and I will be

be yours for all e-ter-ni-ty.

yours for all e-ter-ni-ty.

85

We trust in you

Finlandia   11 10 11 10 11 10

Words: E A G Cherry (1872–1897)
in this version Jubilee Hymns
Music: from *Finlandia*
J Sibelius (1865–1957)

1 We trust in you, our shield and our de-
2 We trust in you, O Cap - tain of sal -
3 We go in faith, our own great weak - ness
4 We trust in you, our shield and our de-

- fend - er; we do not fight a -
- va - tion! in your dear name, all
feel - ing, and need - ing more each
- fend - er: yours is the tri - umph—

- lone a - gainst the foe: strong in your
o - ther names a - bove: Je - sus our
day your grace to know; yet from our
yours shall be the praise! When pass - ing

strength, safe in your keep - ing ten - der,
right - eous - ness, our sure foun - da - tion,
hearts a song of tri - umph peal - ing,
through the gates of hea - ven's splen - dour,

we trust in you, and in your name we
our prince of glo - ry and our king of
'We trust in you, and in your name we
vic - tors, we rest in you through end - less

go; strong in your strength, safe
love; Je - sus, our right - eous -
go;' yet from our hearts a
days; when pass - ing through the

in your keep - ing ten - der, we trust in
- ness, our sure foun - da - tion, our prince of
song of tri - umph peal - ing, 'We trust in
gates of hea - ven's splen - dour, vic - tors, we

you, and in your name we go.
glo - ry and our king of love.
you, and in your name we go.'
rest in you through end - less days.

86   When all your mercies, O my God

Contemplation   8 6 8 6 (CM)

Words: J Addison (1672–1719)
in this version Jubilate Hymns
Music: F A G Ouseley (1825–1889)

1 When all your mer - cies, O____ my God, my
2 Un - num - bered bless - ings to____ my soul your
3 Ten thou - sand thou - sand pre - cious gifts my

thank - ful soul sur - veys,_____ up - lift - ed by the
ten - der care be - stowed_____ be - fore____ my in - fant
dai - ly thanks em - ploy;_____ nor is____ the least a

view,_ I'm lost in won - der, love____ and praise._____
heart_ per - ceived from whom these bless - ings flowed._____
thank - ful heart that takes_ those gifts____ with joy.____

4   In health and sickness, joy and pain,
     your goodness I'll pursue;
     and after death, in distant worlds,
     the glorious theme renew.

5   Throughout eternity, O Lord,
     a joyful song I'll raise;
     but all eternity's too short
     to utter all your praise!

May the grace of Christ our saviour 87(i)

Halton Holgate 8 7 8 7

Words: from 2 Corinthians 13
J Newton (1725–1807)
Music: melody W Boyce (1711–1779)
harmony S S Wesley (1810–1876)

Quietly

1 May the grace of Christ__ our sav - iour
2 So may we re - main__ in u - nion

and the Fa - ther's bound - less love,__ with__ the__ Ho - ly
with each o - ther and the Lord,__ and__ pos - sess, in

Spi - rit's fa - vour, rest up - on us from__ a - bove.
sweet com - mu - nion, joys which earth can - not__ af - ford.

87(ii) May the grace of Christ our saviour

Waltham 8 7 8 7

Words: from 2 Corinthians 13
J Newton (1725–1807)
Music: H Albert (1604–1651)

Quietly

1 May the grace___ of Christ our sav - iour
2 So may we___ re - main in un - ion

and the Fa - ther's bound - less love, with the Ho - ly
with each o - ther and___ the Lord, and pos - sess, in

Spi - rit's fa - vour, rest up - on us from___ a - bove.
sweet com - mun - ion, joys which earth can - not___ af - ford.

Father God in heaven

88

Kum ba yah 8 8 8 5

Words: from *The Lord's Prayer*
J E Seddon (1915–1983)
Music: traditional melody
arranged David Peacock

1 Fa - ther God in heaven, Lord most high: hear your
2 May your king - dom come here on earth, may your
3 Give us dai - ly bread day by day, and for -

child - ren's prayer, Lord most high; hal-lowed be your name, Lord most
will be done here on earth; as it is in heaven so on
- give our sins day by day, as we too for - give day by

high — O Lord, _____ hear our prayer.
earth — O Lord, _____ hear our prayer.
day — O Lord, _____ hear our prayer.

4 Lead us in your way,
    make us strong,
  when temptations come
    make us strong;
save us all from sin,
    keep us strong —
  O Lord, hear our prayer.

5 All things come from you,
    all are yours —
  kingdom, glory, power,
    all are yours:
take our lives and gifts,
    all are yours —
  O Lord, hear our prayer.

89 Bind us together, Lord

Words and music: Bob Gillman
Music arranged David Peacock

90 Let there be love shared among us

Words and music: Dave Bilbrough

Like a mighty river flowing

91(i)

Quem pastores laudavere 8 8 8 7

Words: Michael Perry
Music: fourteenth-century German melody
arranged John Barnard

1 Like a migh - ty ri - ver flow - ing, like___ a
2 Like the hills se - rene___ and e - ven, like___ the
3 Like the sum - mer breez - es play - ing, like___ the

flower_ in beau - ty grow - ing, far be - yond all
cours - ing clouds of hea - ven, like the heart that's
tall___ trees soft - ly sway - ing, like the lips of

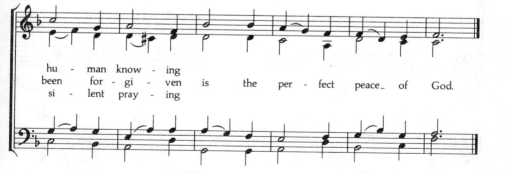

hu - man know - ing
been for - gi - ven is the per - fect peace_ of God.
si - lent pray - ing

4 Like the morning sun ascended,
   like the scents of evening blended,
   like a friendship never ended
   is the perfect peace of God.

5 Like the azure ocean swelling,
   like the jewel all-excelling,
   far beyond our human telling
   is the perfect peace of God.

91(ii)　Like a mighty river flowing

Old Yeavering　8 8 8 7

Words: Michael Perry
Music: Noël Tredinnick

1 Like a migh - ty ri - ver flow - ing, like a
2 Like the hills se - rene and e - ven, like the
(3) Like the sum - mer breez - es play - ing, like the
4 Like the morn - ing sun a - scend - ed, like the
5 Like the a - zure o - cean swell - ing, like the

flower in beau - ty grow - ing, far be - yond all hu - man
cours - ing clouds of hea - ven, like the heart that's been for -
tall trees soft - ly sway - ing, like the lips of si - lent
scents of even - ing blend - ed, like a friend - ship ne - ver
jew - el all - ex - cell - ing, far be - yond our hu - man

know - ing
- gi - ven
pray - ing　is the per - fect peace of God.
end - ed
tell - ing

Verse 3 (melody in tenor)

3 Like the sum - mer breez - es play - ing, like the

like the

tall trees soft - ly sway - ing, like the lips of si - lent

tall trees soft - ly sway - ing, like the lips of si - lent

pray - ing is___ the per - fect peace of God.

pray - ing

92(i)   What a friend we have in Jesus

Blaenwern   8 7 8 7 D

Words: J M Scriven (1819–1886)
Music: W P Rowlands (1860–1937)

1 What a friend we have___ in Je - sus, all our
2 Have we tri - als and___ temp - ta - tions, is there
3 Are we weak and hea - vy - la - den, bur - dened

sins and griefs___ to bear; what a pri - vi -
trou - ble a - ny - where? We should ne - ver
with a load___ of care? Je - sus is our

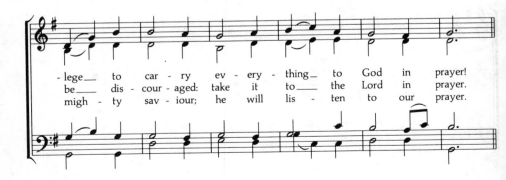

- lege___ to car - ry ev - ery - thing___ to God in prayer!
be___ dis - cour - aged: take it to___ the Lord in prayer.
migh - ty sav - iour; he will lis - ten to our prayer.

O what peace we of - ten for - feit, O what
Can we find a friend so faith - ful who will
Do your friends des - pise, for - sake you? Take it

need - less pain we bear, all be - cause we
all our sor - rows share? Je - sus knows our
to the Lord in prayer: in his arms he

do not car - ry ev - ery - thing to God in prayer.
ev - ery weak - ness — take it to the Lord in prayer.
will en - fold you and his love will shield you there.

92(ii)　What a friend we have in Jesus

Converse　8 7 8 7 D

Words: J M Scriven (1819–1886)
Music: C C Converse (1832–1918)

1 What a friend we have in Je - sus, all our sins and griefs to bear;
2 Have we tri - als and temp - ta - tions, is there trou-ble a - ny - where?
3 Are we weak and hea - vy - la - den, bur - dened with a load of care?

what a pri - vi - lege to car - ry ev - ery-thing to God in prayer!
We should ne - ver be dis - cour - aged: take it to the Lord in prayer.
Je - sus is our migh-ty sav - iour; he will lis - ten to our prayer.

O what peace we of - ten for - feit, O what need-less pain we bear,
Can we find a friend so faith - ful who will all our sor-rows share?
Do your friends des-pise, for - sake you? Take it to the Lord in prayer:

all be - cause we do not car - ry ev - ery-thing to God in prayer.
Je - sus knows our ev-ery weak - ness — take it to the Lord in prayer.
in his arms he will en - fold you and his love will shield you there.

Nice

Now thank we all our God

93(i)

Nun danket   6 7 6 7 6 6 6 6

Words: after M Rinkart (1586–1649)
C Winkworth (1827–1878)
Music: later form of melody by J Crüger (1598–1662)
Descant: David Iliff

1 Now thank we all our God, with hearts and hands and
2 O may this boun-teous God through all our life be

voi - ces, who won-drous things has done, in whom this world re -
near us, to fill our hearts with joy, and send us peace to

- joi - ces; who from our mo-thers' arms has blessed us on our
cheer us; to keep us still in grace, and guide us when per -

way with count-less gifts of love, and still is ours to - day.
- plexed; to free us from all ills in this world and the next.

Verse 3 with descant overleaf

Descant

3 All praise and__ thanks to God who__ reigns in high - est

3 All praise and thanks to God who reigns in high - est

hea - ven; to Fa - ther__ and to Son and Spi - rit now be

hea - ven; to Fa-ther and to Son and Spi - rit now be

gi - ven; to__ the e - ter-nal God, whom heaven and earth_ a -

gi - ven; to the e - ter - nal God, whom heaven and earth a -

- dore: the one who was, is now, and shall_ be ev - er - more.

- dore: the one who was, is now, and shall be ev - er - more.

Now thank we all our God 93(ii)

Gracias 6 7 6 7 6 6 6 6

Words: after M Rinkart (1586–1649)
C Winkworth (1827–1878)
Music: G Beaumont (1903–1970)
arranged John Barnard

1 Now thank we all our God, with hearts and hands and
2 O may this boun-teous God through all our life be
3 All praise and thanks to God who reigns in high-est

voi-ces, who won-drous things has done, in whom this world re -
near us, to fill our hearts with joy, and send us peace to
hea-ven; to Fa-ther and to Son and Spi-rit now be

- joi-ces; who from our mo-thers' arms has blessed us on our
cheer us; to keep us still in grace, and guide us when per -
gi-ven; to the e-ter-nal God, whom heaven and earth a -

way with count-less gifts of love, and still is ours to - day.
- plexed; to free us from all ills in this world and the next.
- dore: the one who was, is now, and shall be ev - er - more.

At the end of the service

94 Praise the Lord, you heavens, adore him

Austria 8 7 8 7 D

Words: from Psalm 148
Foundling Hospital Collection (1796)
Music: Croatian folk tune
adapted F J Haydn (1732–1809)
Descant: T H Ingham (1878–1948) altered

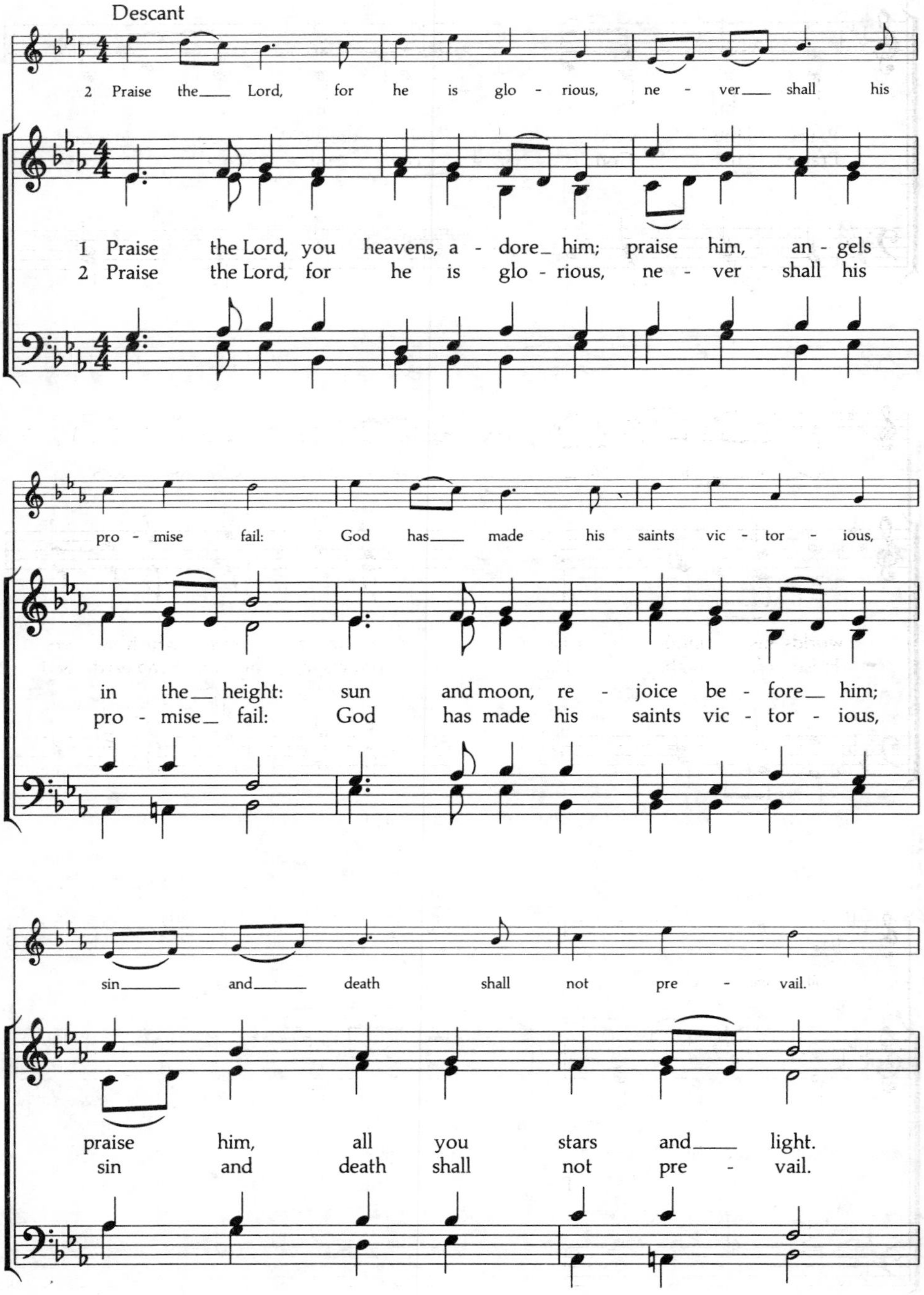

Descant
2 Praise the Lord, for he is glo - rious, ne - ver shall his
1 Praise the Lord, you heavens, a - dore him; praise him, an - gels
2 Praise the Lord, for he is glo - rious, ne - ver shall his
pro - mise fail: God has made his saints vic - tor - ious,
in the height: sun and moon, re - joice be - fore him;
pro - mise fail: God has made his saints vic - tor - ious,
sin and death shall not pre - vail.
praise him, all you stars and light.
sin and death shall not pre - vail.

Praise the God of our sal - va - tion!

Praise the Lord, ___ for he has spo - ken,
Praise the God ___ of our sal - va - tion!

Hosts on ___ high, ___ his ___ power ___ pro - claim; heaven and earth and

worlds his migh - ty voice o - beyed; laws which ne - ver
Hosts on high, his power pro-claim; heaven and earth and

all cre - a - tion praise ___ and ___ glo - ri - fy his name!

shall be bro - ken for their ___ guid - ance ___ he has ___ made.
all cre - a - tion praise and ___ glo - ri - fy his ___ name!

95   Praise to the Lord, the almighty

Lobe den Herren   14 14 4 7 8

Words: from Psalm 103
after J Neander (1650–1680)
C Winkworth (1827–1878) and others
Music: *Stralsund Gesangbuch* 1665
Descant: C S Lang (1891–1971)

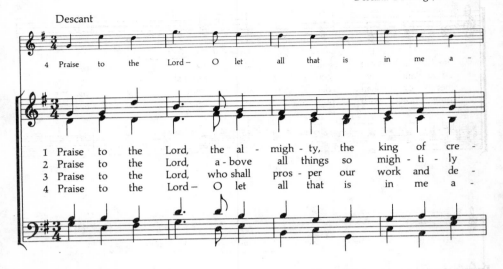

Descant

4 Praise to the Lord — O let all that is in me a -

1 Praise to the Lord, the al - migh - ty, the king of cre -
2 Praise to the Lord, a - bove all things so migh - ti - ly
3 Praise to the Lord, who shall pros - per our work and de -
4 Praise to the Lord — O let all that is in me a -

- dore   him! All that has life and breath,

- a - tion! O my soul, praise him, for
reign - ing; keep - ing us safe at his
- fend us; sure - ly his good - ness and
- dore him! All that has life and breath,

96

Sing praise to the Lord

Laudate Dominum   10 10 11 11

Words: from Psalms 148 and 150
H W Baker (1821–1877)
in this version Jubilate Hymns
Music: C H H Parry (1848–1918)

1 Sing praise to the Lord! Praise him in the
2 Sing praise to the Lord! Praise him up - on
3 Sing praise to the Lord! All things that give
(4) Sing praise to the Lord! Thanks - giv - ing and

height, re - joice in his word you an - gels of
earth in tune - ful ac - cord, you saints of new
sound, each ju - bi - lant chord re - e - cho a -
song, to him be out - poured all a - ges a -

light; you hea - vens, a - dore him by whom you were
birth; praise him who has brought you his grace from a -
- round; loud or - gans, his glo - ry pro - claim in deep
- long; for love in cre - a - tion, for hea - ven re -

made, and wor - ship be - fore him in bright-ness ar - rayed.
- bove, praise him who has taught you to sing of his love.
tone, and sweet harp, the sto - ry of what he has done.
- stored, for grace of sal - va - tion, sing praise to the Lord!

-a - tion,_ for_ hea - ven re - stored, for

grace of sal - va - tion, sing praise to the Lord!

Optional ending (harmony)

(A - men,___ a - men.)

Bring to the Lord a glad new song   97

Jerusalem 8 8 8 8 D (DLM)

Words: from Psalms 149 and 150
Michael Perry
Music: C H H Parry (1848–1918)

Slow but with animation

Bring to the Lord   a glad new song;   child-ren of grace, ex-tol your

king: wor-ship and praise   to God be - long — to in-stru-ments of mu - sic,

sing!   Let those be   warned   who spurn   his   name;   na - tions and

kings,   at - tend his   word —   God's jus - tice   shall   bring ty - rants

shame: let ev-ery   crea-ture praise the   Lord!

Praise him with - in these hal - lowed_ walls, praise him be - neath the dome of heaven; by cym-bals' sounds and trum - pets' calls let prais - es fit for God be

given! With strings and brass and wind re-joice — then, join his praise with full ac-

- cord all liv-ing things with breath and voice: let ev-ery

allargando *ff* *rit.*

crea-ture praise the Lord!

ff

8va

Christ triumphant, ever reigning 98(i)

Christ triumphant 8 5 8 5 7 9

Words: Michael Saward
Music: Michael Baughen
arranged David Wilson

1 Christ tri-umph-ant, ev-er reign-ing, Sav-iour, Mas-ter, King!
2 Word in-car-nate, truth re-veal-ing, Son of Man on earth!
3 Suf-fering ser-vant, scorned, ill-treat-ed, vic-tim cru-ci-fied!

— Lord of heaven, our lives sus-tain-ing, hear us as we
— power and ma-jes-ty con-ceal-ing by your hum-ble
— death is through the cross de-feat-ed, sin-ners jus-ti-

sing: Yours the glo-ry and the crown, the high
birth:
-fied:

re - nown, the e-ter-nal name.

4 Priestly king, enthroned for ever
high in heaven above!
sin and death and hell shall never
stifle hymns of love:
    Yours the glory . . .

5 So, our hearts and voices raising
through the ages long,
ceaselessly upon you gazing,
this shall be our song
    Yours the glory . . .

98(ii)   Christ triumphant, ever reigning

Guiting Power   8 5 8 5 7 9

Words: Michael Saward
Music: John Barnard

Descant

5 Our hearts and voi - ces rai - sing

1 Christ tri - um - phant, ev - er reign - ing,
2 Word in - car - nate, truth re - veal - ing,
3 Suf - fering ser - vant, scorned, ill - treat - ed,
4 Priest - ly king, en - throned for ev - er
5 So, our hearts and voi - ces rais - ing

through the a - ges long,

Sav - iour, Mas - ter, King!
Son of Man on earth!
vic - tim cru - ci - fied!
high in heaven a - bove!
through the a - ges long,

up - on you gaz - ing,

Lord of heaven, our lives sus - tain - ing
power and ma - jes - ty con - ceal - ing
death is through the cross de - feat - ed,
sin and death and hell shall ne - ver
cease - less - ly up - on you gaz - ing,

Organ

99　　Praise the Lord, his glories show

Llanfair　7 7 7 7 and Alleluias

Words: H F Lyte (1793–1847)
Music: R Williams (1781–1821)

1 Praise the Lord, his glo - ries show,
2 Earth to heaven and heaven to__ earth　Al - le - lu - ia,
3 Praise the Lord, his mer - cies trace,

all that lives on earth be - low;
tell his won-ders, sing his__ worth;　al - le - lu - ia,
praise his pro - vi - dence and grace;

an - gels round his throne a - bove,
age to age, and shore to__ shore,　al - le - lu - ia,
all that he for us__ has__ done,

Unison

all who see and share his__ love.
praise him, praise him ev - er - more.　al - le - lu - ia!
all he gives us in his__ Son!

Tell out, my soul

100(i)

Yanworth   10 10 10 10

Words: from Luke 1
(*The Song of Mary / Magnificat*)
Timothy Dudley-Smith
Music: John Barnard

1 Tell out, my soul, the great-ness of the Lord! Un-num - bered bless-ings, give my spi - rit voice; ten - der to me the pro - mise of his word — in God my sav - iour shall my heart re - joice.

2 Tell out, my soul, the great-ness of his name! Make known his might, the deeds his arm has done; his mer - cy sure, from age to age the same — his ho - ly name: the Lord, the migh - ty one.

3 Tell out, my soul, the great-ness of his might! Powers and do - min - ions lay their glo - ry by; proud hearts and stub - born wills are put to flight, the hun - gry fed, the hum - ble lift - ed high.

4 Tell out, my soul, the glo - ries of his word! Firm is his pro - mise, and his mer - cy sure: tell out, my soul, the great - ness of the Lord to child - ren's child - ren and for ev - er - more!

100(ii)

Tell out, my soul

Words: from Luke 1
(*The Song of Mary / Magnificat*)
Timothy Dudley-Smith
Music: W Greatorex (1877–1949)
Descant: David Iliff

Woodlands 10 10 10 10

1 Tell out, my soul, the great-ness of the Lord!
2 Tell out, my soul, the great-ness of his name!
3 Tell out, my soul, the great-ness of his might!

Un - num - bered bless-ings, give my spi - rit voice;
Make known his might, the deeds his arm has done;
Powers and do - min - ions lay their glo - ry by;

ten - der to me the pro - mise of his word —
his mer - cy sure, from age to age the same —
proud hearts and stub - born wills are put to flight,

in God my sav - iour shall my heart re - joice.
his ho - ly name: the Lord, the migh - ty one.
the hun - gry fed, the hum - ble lift - ed high.

101 We really want to thank you, Lord

Words: Ed Baggett
verse 3 after T Ken (1637–1710)
in this version Jubilate Hymns
Music: Ed Baggett
arranged Betty Pulkingham

Verses

1 We thank you, Lord, for your gift to us, your
2 We thank you, Lord, for our life to-ge - ther - to
3 Praise God from whom all bless - ings flow, in

life so rich be - yond com-pare, the gift of your bo - dy
live and move in the love of Christ, your ten - der - ness which
heaven a - bove, and earth be - low; one God, three per - sons,

here on earth of which we sing and share.
sets us free to serve you with our lives.
we a - dore - to him be praise for ev - er - more!

D.C. al Coda

⊕ CODA

king!

At the end of the service

102　　　To God be the glory

To God be the glory　11 11 11 11 and refrain

Words: F J van Alstyne (1820–1915)
Music: W H Doane (1832–1916)
Descant and arrangement: Noël Tredinnick

1 To God be the glory! Great things he has done:
2 O per - fect re - demp - tion, the pur - chase of blood!
(3) Great things he has taught us, great things he has done,

so loved he the world that he gave us his Son
To ev - ery be - liev - er the pro - mise of God:
and great our re - joic - ing through Je - sus the Son:

who yield - ed his life an a - tone - ment for sin,
the vil - est of - fen - der who tru - ly be - lieves,
but pur - er and high - er and great - er will be

and op - ened the life - gate that all may go in.
that mo - ment from Je - sus a par - don re - ceives.
our won - der, our glad - ness, when Je - sus we see!

Chorus

Praise the Lord, praise the Lord! let the earth hear his voice;

praise the Lord, praise the Lord! let the peo - ple re - joice:

O come to the Fa - ther through Je - sus the Son

and give him the glo - ry — great things he has done.

Verse 3 with descant overleaf

Soprano and Alto Descant

great - er will be____ our won - der, our glad - ness, when

great - er will be____ our won - der, our glad - ness, when

Chorus

Je - sus we see! Praise the Lord,____ praise the Lord!____ let the

Je - sus we see! Praise the Lord, praise the Lord! let the

ff

earth hear his voice;____ praise the Lord,____ praise the

earth hear his voice; praise the Lord, praise the

Christ is the king

Vulpius 8 8 8 4

Words: G K A Bell (1883–1958)
Music: M Vulpius (c1560–1616)

1 Christ is the king! O friends re - joice; bro-thers and sis - ters,
2 O mag - ni - fy the Lord, and raise an-thems of joy and
3 They with a faith for ev - er new fol-lowed the king, and

with one voice let the world know he is your choice.
ho - ly praise for Christ's brave saints of an - cient days.
round him drew thou-sands of ser - vants brave and true.

Al - le - lu - ia, al - le - lu - ia, al - le - lu - ia!

4 O Christian women, Christian men,
   all the world over, seek again
   the way disciples followed then.
   Alleluia, alleluia, alleluia!

5 Christ through all ages is the same:
   place the same hope in his great name;
   with the same faith his word proclaim.
   Alleluia, alleluia, alleluia!

6 Let Love's unconquerable might
   your scattered companies unite
   in service to the Lord of light.
   Alleluia, alleluia, alleluia!

7 So shall God's will on earth be done,
   new lamps be lit, new tasks begun,
   and the whole church at last be one.
   Alleluia, alleluia, alleluia!

104   Lord, for the years

Lord of the years   11 10 11 10

Words: Timothy Dudley-Smith
Music: Michael Baughen
arranged David Iliff
verse 5 arranged with descant John Barnard

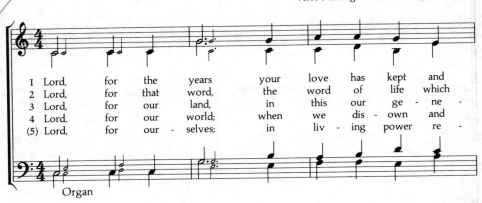

1 Lord,   for   the   years   your   love   has   kept   and
2 Lord,   for   that   word,   the   word   of   life   which
3 Lord,   for   our   land,   in   this   our   ge   - ne -
4 Lord,   for   our   world;   when   we   dis - own   and
(5) Lord,   for   our - selves;   in   liv - ing   power   re -

Organ

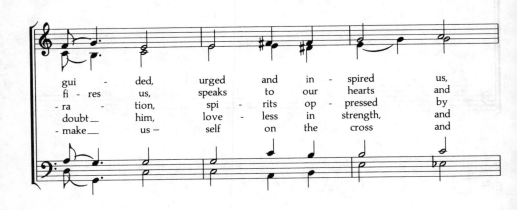

gui - ded,   urged   and   in - spired   us,
fi - res   us,   speaks   to   our   hearts   and
- ra - tion,   spi - rits   op - pressed   by
doubt   him,   love - less   in   strength,   and
- make   us   self   on   the   cross   and

cheered   us   on   our   way;   sought   us   and
sets   our   souls   a - blaze;   teach - es   and
plea - sure,   wealth   and   care;   for   young   and
com - fort - less   in   pain;   hun - gry   and
Christ   up - on   the   throne —   past   put   be -

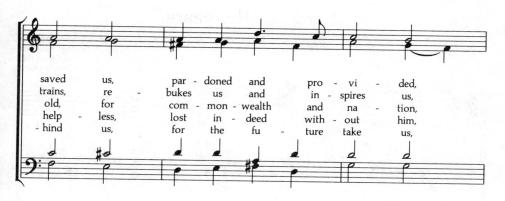

saved us, par - doned and pro - vi - ded,
trains, re - bukes us and in - spires us,
old, for com - mon - wealth and na - tion,
help - less, lost in - deed with - out him,
- hind us, for the fu - ture take us,

Lord of the years, we bring our thanks to - day.
Lord of the word, re - ceive your peo - ple's praise.
Lord of our land, be pleased to hear our prayer.
Lord of the world, we pray that Christ may reign.
Lord of our lives, to live for Christ a - lone.

Descant

5 Lord,____ in liv - ing power re - make____ us –

5 Lord, for our - selves; in liv - ing power re - make us –

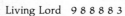

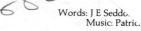

To him we come

Living Lord 9 8 8 8 8 3

Words: J E Seddon
Music: Patric.

With strength
Unison

1 To   him   we   come —   Je - sus
2 In   him   we   live —   Christ   our
3 For   him   we   go —   sol - diers
4 With   him   we   serve —   his   the
5 On - ward we   go —   faith - ful,

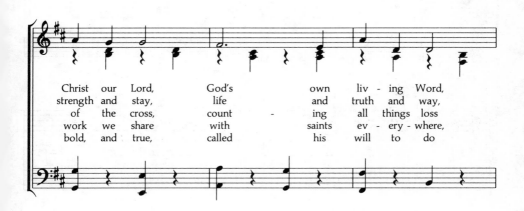

Christ   our   Lord,   God's   own   liv - ing   Word,
strength and   stay,   life   and   truth and   way,
of   the   cross,   count   -   ing   all   things loss
work   we   share   with   saints   ev - ery - where,
bold,   and   true,   called   his   will   to   do

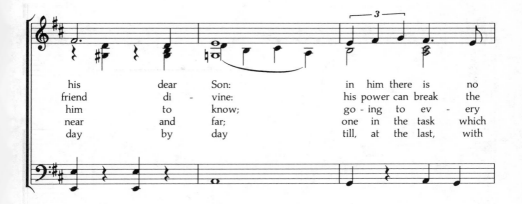

his   dear   Son: in   him there is   no
friend   di   -   vine: his power can break   the
him   to   know;   go - ing   to ev -   ery
near   and   far;   one in   the task   which
day   by   day   till, at   the last,   with

east   and   west,   in   him   all   na - tions   shall   be   blessed;
chains   of   sin,   still   all   life's storms   with - out,   with - in,
land   and   race,   preach-ing   to   all   re - deem - ing   grace,
faith   re - quires,   one   in   the   zeal   which   ne - ver   tires,
joy   we'll   see   Je - sus,   in   glo - rious   ma - jes - ty;

to   all   he   of - fers   peace   and   rest —   lov - ing
help   us   the   dai - ly   fight   to   win —   liv - ing
build - ing   his   church   in   ev - ery   place —   con - quering
one   in   the   hope   his   love   in - spires —   com - ing
live   with   him   through   e - ter - ni - ty —   reign - ing

1-4.   5.

Lord!   Lord!
Lord!
Lord!
Lord!

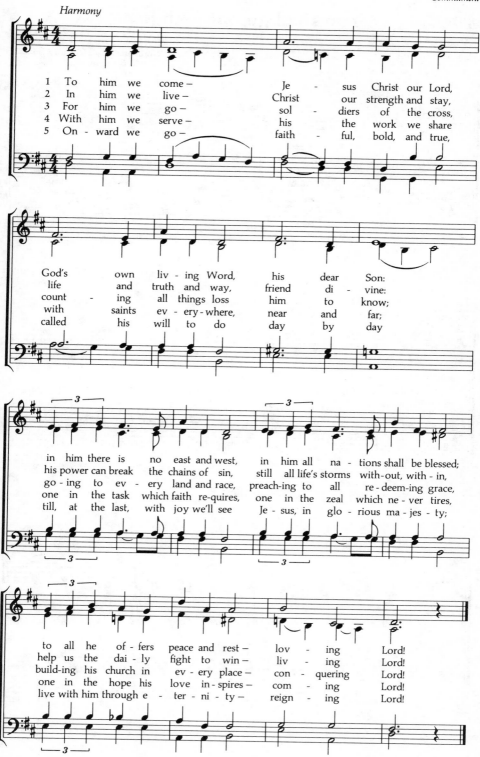

This version is harmonically compatible with the unison setting on the previous pages.

At the end of the service

106 # You shall go out with joy

From Isaiah 55
Words and music: Stuart Dauermann
Music arranged David Peacock

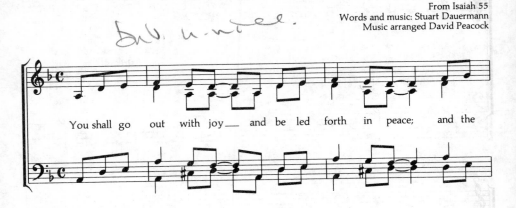

You shall go out with joy— and be led forth in peace; and the

moun-tains and the hills shall break forth be-fore you, sing-ing

songs of joy;— and the trees of the field shall—

Words and music: © 1975 Lillenas Publishing Co / Thankyou Music,
PO Box 75, Eastbourne, East Sussex BN23 6NW

clap, shall clap their hands, and the trees of the field shall

clap their hands, __ and the trees of the field shall

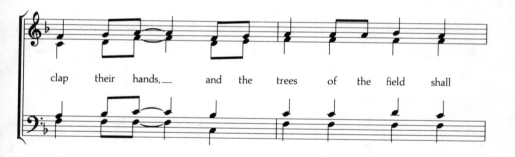

clap their hands, __ and the trees of the field shall

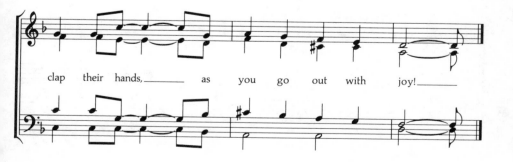

clap their hands, _____ as you go out with joy!_____

Jesus, redeemer, come

Words: Michael Perry
Music: from First Prelude in C
J S Bach (1685–1750)
adapted C F Gounod (1818–1893)
arranged Norman Warren

Ave Maria

Andante

Jesus, redeemer, Mary's child

Ave Maria

Words: Michael Perry
Music: F Schubert (1797–1828)
arranged John Barnard

1 Je - sus, re - deem - er, Ma - ry's child, en - due me with your hum - ble

spi - rit! I live, by mer - cy re - con -

- ciled, and___ all your work of grace in -

- her - - - it. You

come to me from heights of glo - ry, for

2 Je - sus, re - deem - - - er,

clos - - est____

friend, sur - round me_ with your ten - der

lov - ing! From my be - gin - ning to my end you___

lead me on,_ your mer - cy prov - - - ing. Be -

- neath your Cross I stand for - giv - en, where from my sins_ I find re -

- lease and gain the first sure step to hea - ven and

Lord en - thrall me with your per - fect beau - ty! I

see your face, I hear your word, your will be-comes my joy-ful

du - - ty. You brave the hurt this world de-

-vis - es to die for one un-kind, un-true; yet

from your tomb the new day ris - es — and I shall rise to reign with

you: Je - sus, re - deem - -

- er!

rallentando e diminuendo

109(i)

God is love

Words: from *The Alternative Service Book 1980*
Music: John Barnard

God is love, and those who live in

love live in God: and God lives in them.

God is love

Words: from *The Alternative Service Book 1980*
Music: Norman Warren

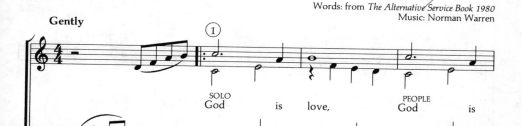

This can also be sung as a canon after the fourth bar,
the piano or organ would then repeat the last four bars on the last time.

Music: Norman Warren / Jubilate Hymns †

110(i)

Blessed are you
WEDDING ACCLAMATIONS

Words: from *The Alternative Service Book 1980*
Music: Norman Warren

Blessed are you,— heaven-ly— Fa-ther; **You give joy to bride-groom and bride.**

Blessed are you, Lord Je - sus Christ: **You have brought new life to man-kind.**

Blessed are you, Ho-ly Spi - rit of God: **You bring us to - ge-ther in love.**

Blessed be Fa-ther, Son and Ho-ly Spi-rit: **One God, to be praised for e - ver. A - men.**

Blessed are you

WEDDING ACCLAMATIONS (CHOIR)

110(ii)

Words: from *The Alternative Service Book 1980*
Music: John Barnard

LEADER
Blessed are you, heaven - ly Father;

CHOIR
mf
You give joy to bride - groom and bride.

LEADER
Blessed are you, Lord Je - sus Christ:

CHOIR
mp
You have brought new life to man - kind.

LEADER
Blessed are you, Holy Spirit of God:

CHOIR
p
You bring us to - ge - ther in love.

LEADER
Blessed be Father, Son and Ho - ly Spirit:

CHOIR
f
One God, to be praised for ev - er. A - men.

Let God be gracious
APPOINTED PSALM

Words: from Psalm 67
from The Liturgical Psalter
David Frost and others

T Hanforth (1867–1948)

J Nares (1715–1783)

1 Let God be gracious to ˈ us and ˈ bless us:
and make his ˈ face ˈ shine upˈon us,

2 that your ways may be ˈ known on ˈ earth:
your liberating ˈ power · aˈmong all ˈ nations.

3 Let the peoples ˈ praise you · O ˈ God:
let ˈ all the ˈ peoples ˈ praise you.

4 Let the nations be ˈ glad and ˈ sing:
**for you judge the peoples with integrity
and govern the ˈ nations · upˈon ˈ earth.**

5 Let the peoples ˈ praise you · O ˈ God:
let ˈ all the ˈ peoples ˈ praise you.

6 Then the earth will ˈ yield its ˈ fruitfulness:
and ˈ God our ˈ God will ˈ bless us.

†7 God ˈ shall ˈ bless us:
and all the ˈ ends · of the ˈ earth will ˈ fear him.

**Glory to the Father and ˈ to the ˈ Son:
and ˈ to the ˈ Holy ˈ Spirit;
as it was in the beˈginning · is ˈ now:
and shall be for ˈ ever. ˈ Aˈmen.**

Words: from *The Psalms: A New Translation for Worship*
© English text 1976, 1977 David L Frost, John A Emerton,
Andrew A Macintosh, all rights reserved
© Pointing 1976, 1977 Wm Collins Sons & Co Ltd,
8 Grafton Street, London W1X 3LA

Chant 1: © 1972 Banks Music Publications

How lovely is your dwelling-place

APPOINTED PSALM

112

Words: from Psalm 84
from The Liturgical Psalter
David Frost and others

C H H Parry (1848–1918)

C H Lloyd (1849–1919)

1 How lovely ˈ is your ˈ dwelling-place:
   O ˈ Lord ˈ God of ˈ hosts!

2 My soul has a desire and longing to enter the ˈ courts · of the ˈ Lord:
   my heart and my flesh reˈjoice · in the ˈ living ˈ God.

3 The sparrow has found her a home
   and the swallow a nest where she may ˈ lay her ˈ young:
   even your altar O Lord of ˈ hosts my ˈ King · and my ˈ God.

4 Blessèd are those who ˈ dwell in · your ˈ house:
   they will ˈ always · be ˈ praising ˈ you.

5 Blessèd is the man whose ˈ strength · is in ˈ you:
   in whose ˈ heart · are the ˈ highways · to ˈ Zion;

6 Who going through the valley of dryness
   finds there a spring from ˈ which to ˈ drink:
   till the autumn ˈ rain shall ˈ clothe it · with ˈ blessings.

†7 They go from ˈ strength to ˈ strength:
   they appear every one of them before the ˈ God of ˈ gods in ˈ Zion.

   Glory to the Father and ˈ to the ˈ Son:
   and ˈ to the ˈ Holy ˈ Spirit;
   as it was in the beˈginning · is ˈ now:
   and shall be for ˈ ever. ˈ Aˈmen.

Note: This Psalm is appointed for the Church of
England 'Series of Dedication after Civil Marriage',
in addition to Psalm 121. It is not therefore
available in the words edition of 'The Wedding Book',
but included here for choir use.

I lift up my eyes
APPOINTED PSALM

Words: from Psalm 121
from The Liturgical Psalter
David Frost and others

Norman Warren

Barry Rose

1 I lift up my ' eyes · to the ' hills:
   but ' where · shall I ' find ' help?

2 My help ' comes · from the ' Lord:
   who has ' made ' heaven · and ' earth.

3 He will not suffer your ' foot to ' stumble:
   and he who watches ' over · you ' will not ' sleep.

4 Be sure he who has ' charge of ' Israel:
   will ' neither ' slumber · nor ' sleep.

5 The Lord him'self · is your ' keeper:
   the Lord is your defence up'on your ' right ' hand;

6 the sun shall not ' strike you · by ' day:
   nor ' shall the ' moon by ' night.

7 The Lord will defend you from ' all ' evil:
   it is ' he · who will ' guard your ' life.

8 The Lord will defend your going out and your ' coming ' in:
   from this time ' forward · for ' ever'more.

   Glory to the Father and ' to the ' Son:
   and ' to the ' Holy ' Spirit;
   as it was in the be'ginning · is ' now:
   and shall be for ' ever. ' A'men.

The chant by Barry Rose was written for
H. M. The Queen's Jubilee Service in St Paul's Cathedral,
7th June 1977. The original key is F major.

Words: from *The Psalms: A New Translation for Worship*
© English text 1976, 1977 David L Frost, John A Emerton,
Andrew A Macintosh, all rights reserved
© Pointing 1976, 1977 Wm Collins Sons & Co Ltd,
8 Grafton Street, London W1X 3LA

Blessed is everyone who fears the Lord 114
APPOINTED PSALM

Words: from Psalm 128
from The Liturgical Psalter
David Frost and others

E F Day (1889–1983)

J Goss (1800–1880)

1 Blessèd is everyone who ǀ fears the ǀ Lord:
and walks in the ǀ confine ǀ of his ǀ ways.

2 You will eat the ǀ fruit of · your ǀ labours:
happy shall you ǀ be and ǀ all · shall go ǀ well with you.

3 Your wife withǀin your ǀ house:
shall ǀ be · as a ǀ fruitful ǀ vine;

4 Your children aǀround your ǀ table:
like the fresh ǀ shoots ǀ of the ǀ olive.

5 Behold thus shall the ǀ man be ǀ blessed:
who ǀ lives · in the ǀ fear · of the ǀ Lord.

6 May the Lord so ǀ bless you · from ǀ Zion:
that you see Jerusalem in prosperity ǀ all the ǀ days of · your ǀ life.

†7 May you see your ǀ children's ǀ children:
and in ǀ Israel ǀ let there · be ǀ peace.

**Glory to the Father and ǀ to the ǀ Son:
and ǀ to the ǀ Holy Spirit;
as it was in the beǀginning · is ǀ now:
and shall be for ǀ ever. ǀ Aǀmen.**

115

Bridal Chorus

from 'Lohengrin'

R Wagner (1813–1883)
arranged John Barnard

"Here comes the Bride

116 Trumpet Voluntary

J Clarke (c1674–1707)
arranged John Barnard

Wedding March

F Mendelssohn (1809–1847)
arranged John Barnard

118   Trumpet Tune in D

H Purcell (1659–1695)
arranged Norman Warren

119 The Arrival of the Queen of Sheba

G F Handel (1685–1759)
arranged Norman Warren

Allegro moderato

120

Processional
from 'The Sound of Music'

R Rodgers (1902–1979)

Maestoso

Air

121

H Purcell (1659–1695)
arranged Norman Warren

122

Finale
from 'The Water Music'

G Handel (1685–1759)
arranged Norman Warren

123

Minuet
'Berenice'

G F Handel (1685–1759)
arranged Norman Warren

124

Air

from 'The Water Music'

G Handel (1685–1759)
arranged Norman Warren

125

Courante

impressive

G Handel (1685–1759)
arranged Norman Warren

126   The Harmonious Blacksmith

G Handel (1685–1759)
arranged Norman Warren

Andante cantabile

(2nd time rall. al fine)

Andante

Preside.

F Mendelssohn (1809–1847)
arranged Norman Warren

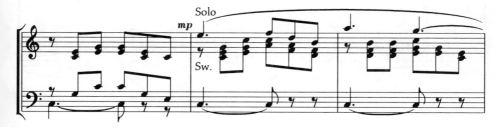

128

Pastorale

'To a Wild Rose'

E MacDowell (1861–1908)
arranged Norman Warren

With simple tenderness

Gymnopédie

E Satie (1866–1925)
arranged Norman Warren

130

Slow Movement
from 'Trumpet Concerto'

F J Haydn (1732–1809)
arranged Norman Warren

131

Pieds-en-l'Air
from 'Capriol Suite'

P Warlock (1894–1930)
arranged Norman Warren

Andante tranquillo

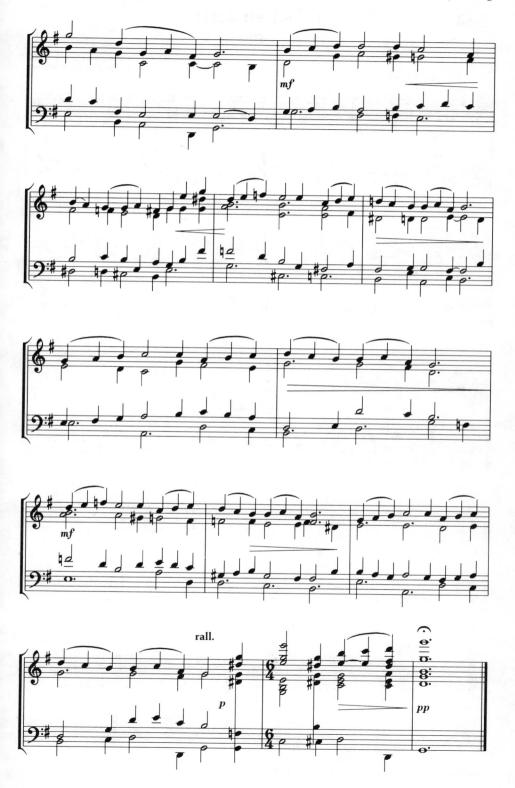

132   **Sicilienne**

M T von Paradis (1759–1824)
arranged Norman Warren

? can't play properly

133

Polovtsian Dance

from 'Prince Igor'

A Borodin (1834–1887)
arranged Norman Warren

Not for a church

Gently

Music arrangement: © Norman Warren / Jubilate Hymns †

Not for a church

Slow Movement
from 'New World' symphony

A Dvořák (1841–1904)
arranged Norman Warren

135 Cavatina

S Myers
arranged Norman Warren

136

Adagio

T Albinoni (1674–1745)
arranged Norman Warren

2nd time rall. al fine

137

Summertime

G Gershwin (1898–1937)
arranged David Iliff

138

Trumpet Minuet

J Clarke (1670–1707)
arranged David Wilson

Sw. contrast

D.%

Flute and 2' or 2⅔' contrast

D.% al Fine

To the Musician

Suggested anthems

    Blessed are the pure in heart – H Walford Davies
    Come Holy Ghost – T Attwood
    Greater love – John Ireland
    If ye love me – Thomas Tallis
    Jesu joy of man's desiring – J S Bach
    Lead me Lord – S S Wesley
    Love one another (Blessed be the God and Father) – S S Wesley
    O Lord increase my faith – Orlando Gibbons
    Rejoice in the Lord alway – Henry Purcell
    The Lord's my shepherd – Brother James Air

Most of these are published by Novello or Oxford University Press.
Many are in the Church Anthem Book (Oxford University Press).

Suggested performance songs included in this volume

    Bind us together – Bob Gillman (89)
    Jesus, redeemer, come (Ave Maria) – Perry / Bach / Gounod (107)
    Jesus, redeemer, Mary's child (Ave Maria) – Perry / Schubert (108)
    Day by day – Richard of Chichester / Norman Warren (80)
    Jesus stand among us at the meeting of our lives – Graham Kendrick (13)
    Let there be love – Dave Bilbrough (90)
    Make me a channel of your peace – Sebastian Temple (70)
    O Holy Spirit breathe on me – Norman Warren (74)
    The new commandment – arranged Norman Warren (11)

Suggested organ voluntaries

    Choral Song – S S Wesley
    Minuet (No 2) Royal Fireworks Suite – Handel
    Nun danket – Karg-Elert
    Toccata in F – Widor
    Toccata in G – Dubois
    Trumpet Tune – Jeremiah Clarke
    Trumpet Tune in D – Henry Purcell
    Trumpet Voluntary in D – John Stanley
    Tuba Tune – C S Lang
    Wedding March – Basil Harwood
            (Pending republication, available from: Public Trust Office, Trust Division,
            Stewart House, Kingsway, London WC2B 6JX)

Organ Albums (simple organ arrangements) – Oxford University Press
Organ Arrangements – Novello

To the Bride and Groom

Using the service

Most ministers in the Church of England will be only too happy to use the most attractive Marriage Service at the beginning of *The Wedding Book*. Of all the new Church of England services it has been the one most universally welcomed. Many Free Church Ministers will also be happy to use it – or their own similar service, because the churches talk together about their services when they are being written.

It comes from 'The Alternative Service Book 1980', approved by the General Synod of The Church of England and by English Act of Parliament. It preserves the traditional dignity yet, at the same time, has a clarity and warmth about it. The setting out of the principles and duties of marriage at the beginning surpasses anything that went before. The pattern of the rest is essentially the same as it has always been.

One attractive feature of the service is that the couple turn and make their promises to each other (rather than to the vicar!). Another is that they both say the words when the ring(s) is exchanged. It is likely that the minister will not use the passage where the bride promises to 'obey' unless the couple themselves ask for it – something to think about! Just for your peace of mind, you can be sure that the minister will say all the words for you to copy, and prompt you quietly throughout the whole service. You don't have to remember any of it by heart – or even read it on the day.

We do suggest, however that you read very carefully through the service to get ready. And especially to discover quite what is so special about Christian Marriage. Many churches lay on a marriage discussion evening or preparation course – usually with other couples about to be married. Most couples who have been say they find it very helpful. Do enquire, so that you don't miss out on this.

Choosing the hymns

Your minister and organist will advise you upon the choice of hymns and music. How many hymns you have depends on what you agree with them, and on how much your invited congregation will want to sing. If a lot of them attend church, three hymns might be the right number. If only a few of them, just two.

If you look at the service at the beginning of the book, you will see that the usual places for hymns are marked. Again, do take the advise of the minister because local situations vary. The size of the church building, the presence or absence of a choir, the position of reading and sermon, or when the register is signed – all these things can affect where the hymns come – and the minister will tell you.

To help you get your choices right, we have placed the hymns in the book in a good order for their use. For instance, the ones about love are at the beginning, where the service is all about love. The psalm versions and the prayerful hymns are in the middle, where the psalms come, along with the prayers for your marriage. Then the celebration hymns are at the end. A good balance would be one hymn from each of these three groups.

There are popular hymns about many Christian subjects – but do try to choose at least one which has something to say about marriage and dedication. You might like to have one of the quiet prayer-hymns in the middle. Some ministers are happy to treat them as a prayer, with the congregation kneeling, or sitting with heads bowed as they are singing to God and praying for you. And the accompanist, if warned, will play gently, to create the right atmosphere.

Don't be put off if you like the words but can't read music and so don't know what tunes they will go to. Usually, the minister or organist will be only too happy to sing or play the various tunes to you. We have set the new wedding hymns to the better known tunes to help your guests.

You may particularly like a tune you have heard, but then discover that the usual words have nothing to do with weddings! Don't worry. Ask the minister or organist to look up the tune in the music edition index to see if it is there set to wedding words, or words more suitable for worship.

Choosing the music

The following list will help you to discuss with the organist your mutual choice of music for the voluntaries. All these pieces are available in the music edition of *The Wedding Book* (to which the numbers refer), along with a list of other wedding music widely available.

Before the Service
Adagio — Albinoni (136)
Air (from The Water Music) — Handel (124)
Air — Henry Purcell (121)
Andante — Mendelssohn (127)
Brother James' Air — Macbeth Bain (29i)
Cavatina — Myers (135)
Courante — Handel (125)
Finale (from The Water Music) — Handel (122)
Gymnopédie — Erik Satie (129)
Minuet (Berenice) — Handel (123)
New World Symphony (Slow Movement) — Dvořák (134)
Pastorale: To a Wild Rose — Edward MacDowell (128)
Pieds-en-l'Air (from Capriol Suite) — Peter Warlock (131)
Polovtsian Dance (from Prince Igor) — Borodin (133)
Sicilienne — Paradis (132)
Skye Boat Song — Scottish traditional (77)
Summertime — Gershwin (137)
The Harmonious Blacksmith — Handel (126)
Trumpet Concerto (Slow Movement) — Haydn (130)

During the signing of the Register
Adagio — Albinoni (136)
Air — Henry Purcell (121)
Air (from The Water Music) — Handel (124)
Andante — Mendelssohn (127)
Ave Maria — Bach / Gounod (107)
Ave Maria — Schubert (108)
Brother James' Air — Macbeth Bain (29i)
Courante — Handel (125)
Gymnopédie — Erik Satie (129)
Minuet (Berenice) — Handel (123)
New World Symphony (Slow Movement) — Dvořák (134)
Pastorale: To a Wild Rose — Edward MacDowell (128)
Pieds-en-l'Air (from Capriol Suite) — Peter Warlock (131)
Polovtsian Dance (from Prince Igor) — Borodin (133)
Sicilienne — Paradis (132)
Skye Boat Song — Scottish traditional (77)
Summertime — Gershwin (137)
The Harmonious Blacksmith — Handel (126)
Trumpet Concerto (Slow Movement) — Haydn (130)

Bridal March — processional
Arrival of the Queen of Sheba — Handel (119)
Bridal Chorus (Lohengrin) — Wagner (115)
Finale (from The Water Music) — Handel (122)
Trumpet Minuet — Jeremiah Clarke (138)
Trumpet Tune in D — Henry Purcell (118)
Trumpet Voluntary — Jeremiah Clarke (116)

Wedding March — recessional
Arrival of the Queen of Sheba — Handel (119)
Finale (from The Water Music) — Handel (122)
Jerusalem — Parry (97)
Processional (from The Sound of Music) — Richard Rodgers (120)
Trumpet Tune in D — Henry Purcell (118)
Trumpet Voluntary — Jeremiah Clarke (116)
Wedding March — Mendelssohn (117)

The editors of *The Wedding Book*, who are themselves both Church of England ministers and enjoy taking many weddings, congratulate you both on your coming marriage, and hope that you and your friends will find this selection of music enhances your very happy occasion. May God bless you.

Michael Perry and Norman Warren

Legal Information

Index relating the hymns to the readings of the Marriage Service (ASB 1980)

Italics indicate hymns specifically based on the reading

From the Old Testament

Genesis 1.26-28, 31a
2 – All creatures of our God and King
4 – Jesus shall reign
5 – Immortal, invisible
20 – For the beauty of the earth
21 – Morning has broken
23 – Great is your faithfulness
58 – God of all living
67 – Lord of creation

From the New Testament

Romans 12.1, 2, 9-13
15 – O God beyond all praising
17 – Your love, O God, has called us here
19 – Amazing grace
37 – O worship the King
54 – Help us to help each other
59 – Happy the home
61 – Take our lives and let them be
65 – Lord Jesus, you have won our hearts
68 – How blessed are those who trust in God
70 – Make me a channel of your peace
71 – Breathe on me, breath of God
75 – O Lord, who came from realms above
76 – O thou who camest from above
79 – Lord of all power
83 – All for Jesus
84 – Take my life and let it be
101 – We really want to thank you, Lord

1 Corinthians 13
9 – *Holy Spirit, gracious guest*
10 – Love divine, all loves excelling
12 – *Faith is your gift, Lord God*
14 – Surprised by joy

Ephesians 3.14-end
1 – Praise, my soul, the king of heaven
10 – Love divine, all loves excelling
15 – O God beyond all praising
17 – Your love, O God, has called us here
19 – Amazing grace
28 – The king of love my shepherd is
29 – The Lord's my shepherd
30 – Through all the changing scenes of life
33 – May God be gracious
37 – O worship the King

47 – O perfect love
60 – Join with us, friends, today
66 – Lord of all hopefulness
73 – Come down, O Love divine
81 – Fill now my life
89 – Bind us together, Lord
93 – Now thank we all our God
105 – To him we come

Ephesians 5.21-33
13 – Jesus, stand among us at the meeting of our lives
16 – Sing out in gladness
27 – To Cana's wedding-feast
41 – Bless all who trust in God
54 – Help us to help each other, Lord
55 – May the mind of Christ (wedding version)
56 – Eternal Father, Lord of life
58 – God of all living
59 – Happy the home
65 – Lord Jesus, you have won our hearts
69 – May the mind of Christ (standard version)
71 – Breathe on me, breath of God
82 – Lord Jesus Christ, you have come to us
87 – May the grace of Christ our saviour
88 – Father God in heaven
100 – Tell out, my soul, the greatness of the Lord
102 – To God be the glory

Colossians 3.12-17
13 – Jesus, stand among us at the meeting of our lives
14 – Surprised by joy
16 – Sing out in gladness
27 – To Cana's wedding-feast
35 – How lovely is your dwelling-place
44 – How good a thing
45 – Jesus the Lord of love and life
54 – Help us to help each other, Lord
55 – May the mind of Christ (wedding version)
59 – Happy the home
69 – May the mind of Christ (standard version)
70 – Make me a channel of your peace
72 – Dear Lord and Father of mankind
81 – Fill now my life
87 – May the grace of Christ our saviour
91 – Like a mighty river flowing

93 – Now thank we all our God
95 – Praise to the Lord, the almighty
100 – Tell out, my soul, the greatness of the Lord

1 John 4.7-12

8 – God is love
10 – Love divine, all loves excelling
15 – O God beyond all praising
17 – Your love, O God, has called us here
18 – Where may that love be found
71 – Breathe on me, breath of God
73 – Come down, O Love divine
87 – May the grace of Christ our saviour
90 – Let there be love shared among us

From the Gospels

Matthew 7.21, 24-27

38 – I will lift up my eyes to the hills
39 – I lift up my eyes to the quiet hills
40 – Unto the hills around me
41 – Bless all who trust in God
42 – Blessed are those who fear the Lord
43 – To set their hearts on God
46 – Lord Jesus Christ, invited guest and saviour

68 – How blessed are those who trust in God
78 – Christ is our corner-stone

Mark 10.6-9

16 – Sing out in gladness
20 – For the beauty of the earth
27 – To Cana's wedding-feast
41 – Bless all who trust in God
54 – Help us to help each other, Lord

John 2.1-11

16 – Sing out in gladness
25 – *Jesus come! for we invite you*
26 – *Jesus, Lord, we pray*
27 – *To Cana's wedding-feast*
46 – *Lord Jesus Christ, invited guest*
49 – *May Christ, the Lord of Cana's feast*

John 15.9-12

11 – *The new commandment*
13 – Jesus, stand among us at the meeting of our lives
14 – Surprised by joy
17 – Your love, O God, has called us here
18 – Where may that love be found
90 – Let there be love shared among us
98 – Christ triumphant, ever reigning
106 – You shall go out with joy

Index to psalm versions
and hymns based on psalms

* indicates psalms appointed in The Marriage Service (ASB 1980)
† indicates psalms appointed in
'Services of Prayer and Dedication After a Civil Marriage'

Index to authors and originators of texts

Italicised numbers indicate originators

Index to composers and arrangers of tunes

Italicised numbers indicate arrangers

Index to organ voluntaries

Index to all melodies
with first lines of hymns and psalms

Asterisk * indicates descant available

General Index

Italics indicate titles or earlier first lines
Asterisk * indicates descant available

<u>Possible</u> 1, 2, 5, 10(ii), 15, 17, 18(i), ?20(i), 21 (same as 58)

(Techn) (Rich) (Richard)
S/N.

22 (i), 22 (ii), (24 #), (28(ii)), (29 *), (29 ii S/N), 37
& choir

41(i), 43, 44(ii), 49, 50, 62, (63, 64)
same   same   same
as 72

(66 & 69 *), 71(i), 74. choir, 78, (79 * 066), 81,

(82 slow °105 * wonderful), 91(i), 92 ii, (93), 94, (95 S/N *)
, intrusing

98(ii), (105 082 Wonderful), 106 Introducing

<u>Against</u> ? Great Prelude
122 Ina G Wedding Handel R
118   " D Purcell (OUT slow) (IN)

Against 116 Trumpet Vol. Clark.
Leave č Mendelssohn Wedding March (17

(Play 3 together)

" Glorious things of thee are
spoken "